2003-2004 EDITION

HIGH FLIERS

www.reuters.com/careers

**HIGH FLIERS PUBLICATIONS LTD
IN ASSOCIATION WITH THE TIMES**

Published by High Fliers Publications Limited
10a Belmont Street, Camden Town, London NW1 8HH
Telephone: 020 7428 9100
Web: www.highfliers.co.uk

Editor Martin Birchall
Publishing Manager Gill Thomas
Production Manager Dave Powell
Portrait Photography Ian Scaramanga & Ben Schott

Printed and bound in Denmark by Nørhaven Book, Viborg.

A CIP catalogue record for this book
is available from the British Library.

ISBN 0 9536991 4 5

Contents

Employer Entries

Information Request Service 160

Find out more about Britain's top employers and you could start your career £5,000 richer!

Foreword

by Tony Halpin
Education Editor, The Times

Welcome to the fifth annual edition of The Times Top 100 Graduate Employers book, containing all the essential information you need on Britain's top employers of graduates in 2003-2004.

This guide provides a unique snapshot of the United Kingdom's most desirable graduate employers, based on the largest survey of university students ever conducted. We interviewed more than 15,400 final year students, accounting for one in five of those who graduated from UK universities in the summer of 2003, and asked them which organisations they believed offered the best opportunities for graduates.

They named over 350 employers from every conceivable sector of business activity, ranging from the civil service and other public bodies to banks and financial services companies, major consumer goods producers, high street retailers, and the military. The 100 organisations named most often by students are listed here in The Times Top 100 Graduate Employers for 2003-2004.

Judging from their responses to the survey, this has been a tough year for graduate job seekers. The 'Class of 2003' was far gloomier than recent predecessors about their job prospects, and more pessimistic than was justified by the true condition of the graduate employment market. Over half of finalists believed there were not enough graduate jobs available and a further third thought the opportunities were very limited this year. Only 37 per cent expected to start a graduate job after leaving university and a record 24 per cent of finalists were planning postgraduate study as an alternative to employment.

Analysis of the employment market showed such pessimism to be largely unwarranted, even if finalists felt they had to start their career hunt earlier and make more applications. Around 5,000 British and international employers hire UK graduates and more than 1,000 of them actively pursue finalists through visits to institutions, recruitment campaigns, and representation via university careers services. Up to 150 different employers are expected to make campus presentations or attend careers fairs at many of the universities which are most popular with graduate recruiters. The virtual presence of employers through the internet continues to grow in importance for the webwise generation of students. More than three-quarters of finalists said they visited graduate recruitment websites during their job searches.

Students' sensitivity to events beyond campus was demonstrated by the decline of investment banks in this year's rankings, as finalists picked up on news of job losses and falling vacancy levels in the financial sector. But fewer opportunities here and in the consulting industry, another major traditional recruiter of graduates, were largely offset by expansion in retailing, the public sector and several other areas, so that the end result was only a small overall decline in vacancies.

The sense of straitened times led to more modest ambitions when it came to starting salaries. The average expected by finalists in 2003, at £18,500, was actually £200 less than for those seeking their first job in 2002.

Meanwhile, student debt is at record levels at an average of £10,100 for this year's graduates. Again, students' pessimism about their prospects was at odds with the reality, which showed that average starting salaries rose by over four per cent to go above £20,000 for the first time this year. This figure masked considerable variation, however, with some employers offering starting salaries below £15,000 and a fortunate four per cent of graduates signing on for more than £30,000. Two-thirds of employers set their salary levels at between £17,500 and £22,500, comfortably within the range finalists said they expected.

If confidence among finalists was low, interest in the range of potential career opportunities was as great as ever. The civil service was named the leading graduate employer for the first time and there was a strong growth of interest in teaching, particularly the new Teach First initiative.

The top choices for 2003 included media, marketing, and consulting, all of which attracted high numbers of applications for limited numbers of vacancies. The largest number of vacancies were in accountancy, law, information technology, general management, retail, and science research and development.

Oddly, applications to IT, consulting, and research and development fell sharply, suggesting that finalists enjoyed a greater chance of success in these areas this year

despite the general gloom of job prospects.

Choosing the right career sector will be the key for the 'Class of 2004'. All the indications are that the levels of vacancies and starting salaries in most career sectors will be broadly similar to this year. Finalists who have their sights set on particular employers might do well to research a less high-profile function within major companies as a route in to a graduate position. All the evidence suggests, however, that the demand for good graduates remains strong and that the personal, professional, and financial rewards offered over the long term far outweigh any short-term uncertainty in the job market.

The Times Top 100 Graduate Employers will help you to research the best options for you. It provides the perfect starting point if you want to discover how the UK's most highly regarded graduate employers recruit their new talent. The directory provides details of their graduate programmes, the functions they recruit for, and when to make applications.

Leaving the familiar routines of university life and taking the first step along a career path can be a daunting process. The decisions you make now will be among the most important you have ever taken. It is a challenge filled with exciting possibilities if you take advantage of all the available information to understand clearly the career opportunities that different employers have to offer.

This book is a celebration of the employers judged by the students themselves to provide the brightest prospects for future careers. Whether by the quality of their training and development programmes, the business success that they enjoy, the scale of their organisations, or by the impression their recruitment activities have made, these are the 100 employers that are most appealing to graduates in 2003.

THE WORLD'S FLAT AND THE MOON'S MADE OF CHEESE.

PRICEWATERHOUSECOOPERS

TAX AND LEGAL SERVICES – NATIONWIDE

Okay, maybe you don't believe us. But go back several hundred years and a lot of people would have taken our comments as gospel. You see, throughout time in the absence of hard facts, humankind has always made broad generalisations. And silly as it sounds, in today's age of information, we're still doing it.

For example, if we asked you what a career in tax would be like, what would you think? Endless mounds of tax returns to be filed? That's a common belief. It's also one that couldn't be further from the truth. The reality is that, at PricewaterhouseCoopers, our tax consultants are pushed to their limits rather than behind desks pushing pens.

As the tax and legal arena grows ever more complex, our clients are demanding increasingly creative approaches. So our graduates find themselves immersed in wider business issues, advising on a huge range of subjects. A far cry from the common perception of what tax is all about.

So before you decide on your career direction, visit our website for all the facts about tax. You may be surprised at what you learn.

www.pwc.com/uk/careers/

Or you can call:
Freephone 0808 100 1500 or
tel: +44 (0)121 265 5852.

Please quote **ref. GRTT0309**

Make it happen.

Over 200 starring roles.
11 gripping storylines.
1 big idea.

Enjoy expert career direction in any one of our 11 business areas.
See our entry later in this book or go straight to our website.

www.rbs.co.uk/graduates

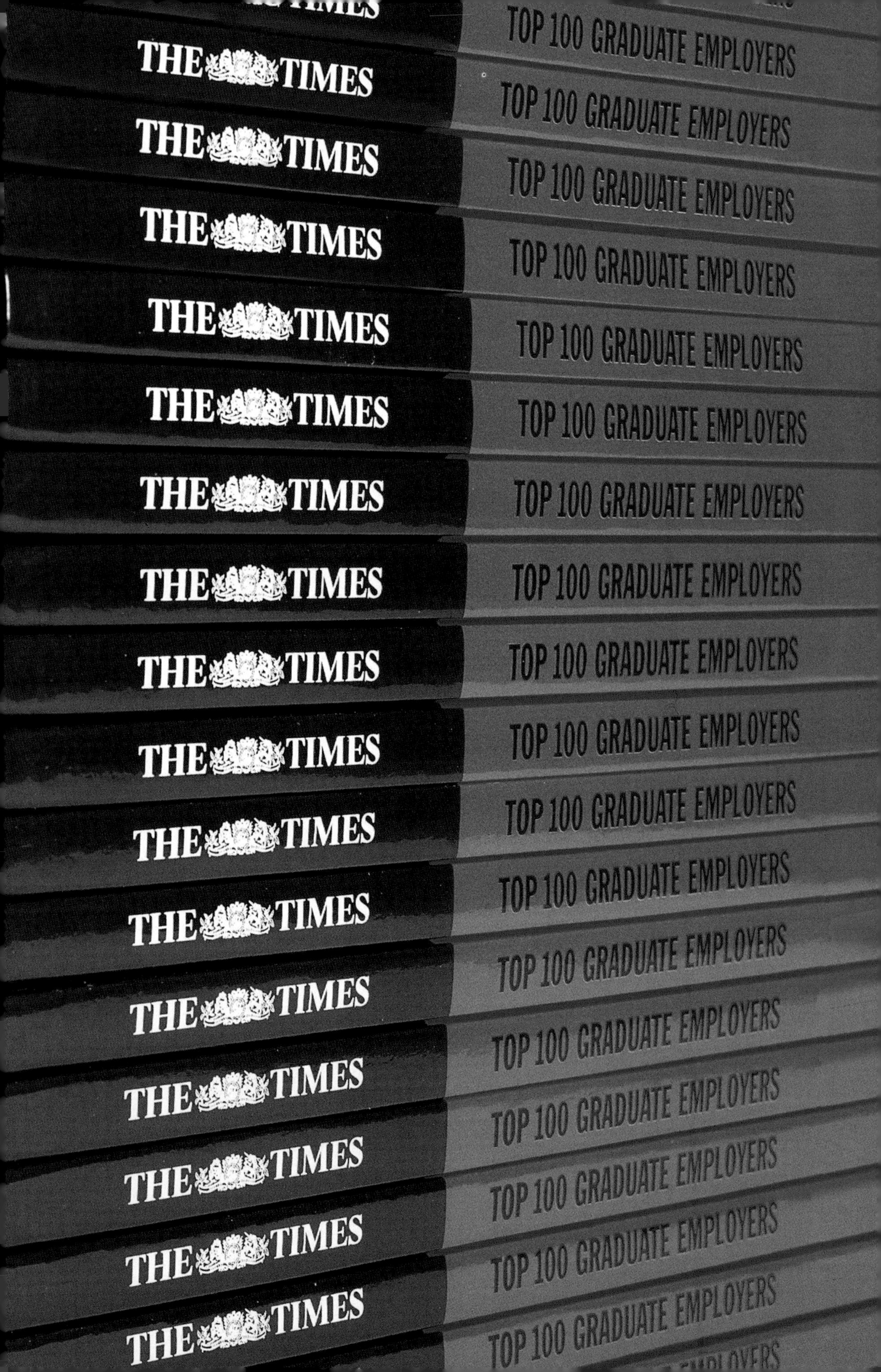
THE TIMES
TOP 100 GRADUATE EMPLOYERS

Compiling the Top 100 Graduate Employers

by Martin Birchall
Survey Director, High Fliers Research Ltd

Anyone in their final year of studies or who has just left university has a wide choice of prospective employers. Despite the recent pessimism in the graduate recruitment market, there are well over five thousand organisations expecting to recruit graduates from UK universities during 2003-2004.

Such choice can be daunting though and makes selecting the employer that is right for you much more difficult. How should you evaluate all the different opportunities and what determines which employers offer the best graduate positions? What are the main criteria that you can use to assess so many organisations and jobs?

There are no simple answers to these questions and clearly no one organisation can ever hope to be right for every graduate. Everyone makes their own judgements about the employers they want to work for and the types of job they find the most attractive.

So how can anyone produce a meaningful league table of the leading employers? What criteria can define whether one organisation is 'better' than another? Well, to compile **The Times Top 100 Graduate Employers**, the independent market research company, High Fliers Research Ltd, interviewed 15,474 final year students leaving university in the summer of 2003. The students from the 'Class of 2003' who took part in the study were selected at random to represent the full population of final-year students, not just those who had been looking for graduate jobs or had already secured employment for after graduation. The research examined students' experiences during their search for a graduate job and asked them about their attitudes to employers.

The key question used to produce the Top 100 was: "Which employer do you consider offers the best opportunities for graduates?" This was an open-ended question and students were not prompted or directed in any way for their answers. Across the whole survey, finalists named more than 350 different employers – from the smallest local firms to some of the world's best-known companies. The responses were analysed to identify the number of times each employer was mentioned, and the one hundred organisations named most often form **The Times Top 100 Graduate Employers** for 2003.

It is clear from the wide range of answers given by finalists in the 'Class of 2003' that individual students used very different criteria to determine which employer they considered offered the best opportunities for graduates. Some focused on employers' general reputations – their public image, their business profile or their commercial success. These views were often greatly coloured by media coverage or by students' experiences as consumers, and finalists used these impressions to define what they thought of the organisations as potential employers.

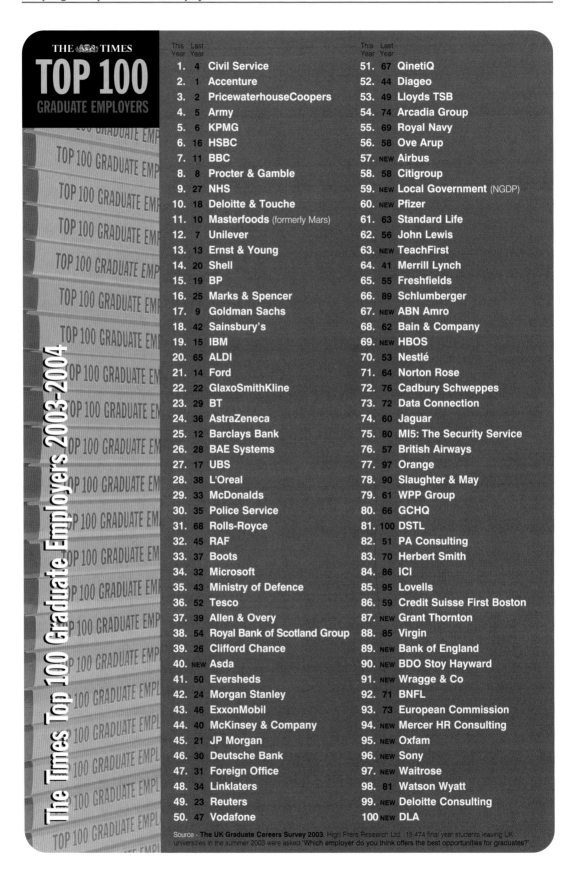

THE ⚜ TIMES

TOP 100
GRADUATE EMPLOYERS

The Times Top 100 Graduate Employers 2003-2004

This Year	Last Year		This Year	Last Year	
1.	4	Civil Service	51.	67	QinetiQ
2.	1	Accenture	52.	44	Diageo
3.	2	PricewaterhouseCoopers	53.	49	Lloyds TSB
4.	5	Army	54.	74	Arcadia Group
5.	6	KPMG	55.	69	Royal Navy
6.	16	HSBC	56.	58	Ove Arup
7.	11	BBC	57.	NEW	Airbus
8.	8	Procter & Gamble	58.	58	Citigroup
9.	27	NHS	59.	NEW	Local Government (NGDP)
10.	18	Deloitte & Touche	60.	NEW	Pfizer
11.	10	Masterfoods (formerly Mars)	61.	63	Standard Life
12.	7	Unilever	62.	56	John Lewis
13.	13	Ernst & Young	63.	NEW	TeachFirst
14.	20	Shell	64.	41	Merrill Lynch
15.	19	BP	65.	55	Freshfields
16.	25	Marks & Spencer	66.	89	Schlumberger
17.	9	Goldman Sachs	67.	NEW	ABN Amro
18.	42	Sainsbury's	68.	62	Bain & Company
19.	15	IBM	69.	NEW	HBOS
20.	65	ALDI	70.	53	Nestlé
21.	14	Ford	71.	64	Norton Rose
22.	22	GlaxoSmithKline	72.	76	Cadbury Schweppes
23.	29	BT	73.	72	Data Connection
24.	36	AstraZeneca	74.	60	Jaguar
25.	12	Barclays Bank	75.	80	MI5: The Security Service
26.	28	BAE Systems	76.	57	British Airways
27.	17	UBS	77.	97	Orange
28.	38	L'Oreal	78.	90	Slaughter & May
29.	33	McDonalds	79.	61	WPP Group
30.	35	Police Service	80.	66	GCHQ
31.	68	Rolls-Royce	81.	100	DSTL
32.	45	RAF	82.	51	PA Consulting
33.	37	Boots	83.	70	Herbert Smith
34.	32	Microsoft	84.	86	ICI
35.	43	Ministry of Defence	85.	95	Lovells
36.	52	Tesco	86.	59	Credit Suisse First Boston
37.	39	Allen & Overy	87.	NEW	Grant Thornton
38.	54	Royal Bank of Scotland Group	88.	85	Virgin
39.	26	Clifford Chance	89.	NEW	Bank of England
40.	NEW	Asda	90.	NEW	BDO Stoy Hayward
41.	50	Eversheds	91.	NEW	Wragge & Co
42.	24	Morgan Stanley	92.	71	BNFL
43.	46	ExxonMobil	93.	73	European Commission
44.	40	McKinsey & Company	94.	NEW	Mercer HR Consulting
45.	21	JP Morgan	95.	NEW	Oxfam
46.	30	Deutsche Bank	96.	NEW	Sony
47.	31	Foreign Office	97.	NEW	Waitrose
48.	34	Linklaters	98.	81	Watson Wyatt
49.	23	Reuters	99.	NEW	Deloitte Consulting
50.	47	Vodafone	100.	NEW	DLA

Source - **The UK Graduate Careers Survey 2003**. High Fliers Research Ltd. 15,474 final year students leaving UK universities in the summer 2003 were asked 'Which employer do you think offers the best opportunities for graduates?'

Others evaluated employers based on the information they had seen during their job search – the quality of recruitment promotions, the impression they had formed from meeting employers when they visited universities, or their experiences through the selection and assessment process. Finalists also considered the number of vacancies that organisations were advertising as an indicator of graduates' prospects, or were influenced by the level of publicity they had seen for employers on campus.

Furthermore, many used the 'employment proposition' as their main guide – the quality of graduate training & development that an employer promises, the remuneration package available, and the practical aspects of a first job such as location or working hours.

Regardless of the criteria that students used to arrive at their answer, the hardest part for many was just selecting a single organisation – choosing two or three, or even half a dozen employers in many ways would have been easier. But the whole purpose of the exercise was to replicate the reality that everybody faces – you can only work for one organisation – and at each stage of the job search there are difficult decisions to be made as to which direction to take and which employers to pursue.

The resulting Top 100 is a dynamic league table of the UK's most exciting and well-respected graduate recruiters in 2003. It is headed for the first time by the Civil Service, which has been rated the UK's top graduate recruiter after increasing their vote by nearly one third since last year. This means that after five consecutive years at number one, Accenture has slipped into second place. In 2003, just under five per cent of finalists voted for the Civil Service, who were ranked fourth in 2002.

Elsewhere in the top ten, there have been several changes. PricewaterhouseCoopers, one of the UK's largest recruiters of graduates, have dropped back one place to 3rd, whilst the Army and KPMG have moved up to 4th and 5th places respectively. Last year's number three employer, Andersen, were taken over in the UK by rival professional services firm Deloitte & Touche during the course of last year. The combined firm is ranked in 10th place this year.

HSBC have climbed ten places to appear at number six, their first time inside the top ten, and have been joined by the NHS who have jumped an impressive eighteen places to reach 9th place. The BBC moved up four to number seven, just ahead of Procter & Gamble who are unchanged in 8th place. Mars and Unilever, the fast-moving consumer goods companies, have both slipped out of the top ten for the first time and are ranked 11th and 12th respectively. Both Shell and BP have climbed inside the top twenty to reach 14th and 15th positions.

Almost all the investment banks who appear in this year's Top 100 have fallen a number of places. Last year's highest rated bank, Goldman Sachs, has dropped to 17th place, whilst JP Morgan and Morgan Stanley are no longer ranked inside the top forty employers.

It appears to have been an excellent year for retailers. Marks & Spencer, a former number one employer from 1997, have climbed up to 16th place and Sainsbury's have jumped a further twenty-four places, to number eighteen – their highest-ever position. This year's highest climber is Aldi, who, having entered the Top 100 last year at number sixty-five, have now leapt up to 20th place. Asda is this year's highest 'new entry' and appear at number forty, just behind Tesco who are now in 36th place. The Arcadia Group have improved their ranking to 54th and Waitrose have entered the table at number ninety-seven.

Elsewhere, there are a further fifteen new entries. Airbus, Pfizer, ABN Amro and HBOS are each ranked inside the top seventy and are joined by the Local Government's National Graduate Development Programme in 59th place, and the new Teach First scheme, which despite being in its first year of operation, has appeared at number sixty-three. Further down the table are new entries for accountancy firms Grant Thornton and BDO Stoy Hayward, and the Bank of England, Wragge & Co, Mercer HR Consulting, Oxfam, Sony, Deloitte Consulting and DLA.

Rolls-Royce are one of the year's highest climbers, rising more than thirty places to reach 31st place. Science and technology firm QinetiQ have jumped sixteen places to 51st, whilst Dstl, the Government research agency, has moved up nineteen places to 81st place.

It seems to have been a year of mixed fortunes for the law firms. Clifford Chance, Linklaters, and

Freshfields have each slipped down the rankings, whilst Allen & Overy, Eversheds and Lovells have climbed a number of places.

Overall, this year's Top 100 has recorded some of the most substantial changes since the league table was first published in 1997. It is interesting to note that the only employers who have remained inside the top ten since that first ranking are the Civil Service, Accenture (then Andersen Consulting) and Procter & Gamble.

The Times Top 100 Graduate Employers book is the definitive guide to the best organisations that are recruiting today. It provides recognition for the success that these employers have found with final year students in 2002-2003, and as such is a useful indicator for the next generation of job hunters.

The graduate employment market remains a complex one – the challenge for the 'Class of 2004' will be to decide for themselves which of the many opportunities to grasp. Many of these employers are featured in the 'Employer Entry' section of this book. Starting on page 27, you can see a two-page profile for each organisation. All the employers are listed alphabetically for easy reference.

The editorial part of the entry includes a short description of what the organisation does, their opportunities for graduates and their recruitment programme for 2003-2004. An 'Employer Factfile' for each employer gives details of the number of graduate vacancies, the business functions that graduates are recruited for, likely starting salaries for 2003, the location of graduate vacancies, application deadlines, the universities that the employer is planning to visit during the year and contact details for their recruitment website and graduate brochure.

The 'Employer Factfile' refers to generic careers areas that the employer recruits for, up to a total of sixteen main functions, and the right-hand page of the entry contains a display advert from the employer.

If you would like to find out more about the employers featured in **The Times Top 100 Graduate Employers**, then you can use the book's 'Information Request Service'. You simply register your personal details and the employers you are interested in using the request card that appears opposite Page 160, or go online to www.Top100GraduateEmployers.com. You'll receive email bulletins about the employers, details of their presentations and careers events at your university, and other information about their graduate recruitment. The service is entirely free and you choose which companies you would like to hear about.

Using the 'Information Request Service' enters you into a prize draw to win £5,000. The first 1,000 people to use return their Information Request card or register their details online will receive a special mousemat from The Times.

Information Request Service

- **Choose as many employers as you want**
  You can request information from any or all of the organisations featured in this year's book. Your information will be sent directly from the employers by email, post or via a text message on your mobile phone.

- **Mind the closing date**
  The deadline to request information and be included in the prize draw to win £5,000 is **Wednesday 31st March 2004**. One card per person only.

- **Write clearly and legibly...**
  If we can't read your handwriting we will be unable to process your details.

- **... And don't forget your email address**
  The service primarily operates electronically, so please include a valid email address – preferably one that will still apply once you have graduated.

- **No stamp required**
  If you're posting from the UK, postage on the card is pre-paid.

I want
to be
rewarded.

A history of innovation. A passion for discovery. A culture that encourages you to explore new ideas. These are the qualities that make AstraZeneca different from most large organisations. And the ones that make it such an inspiring place to establish your career.

From day one, we think everyone can contribute. And that everyone can change the way we do things. We don't recruit graduates solely on the strength of past achievements, but rather on their potential and what we think they can achieve.

Whatever your degree and wherever you join us – the work you do here will have a positive impact on your own career and on the lives of other people. To find out more, visit our website www.ideas.astrazeneca.com

AstraZeneca
life inspiring ideas

THE TIMES

TOP 100
GRADUATE EMPLOYERS

THE TIMES

TOP 100
GRADUATE EMPLOYERS

How to use the directory

Many of the employers listed within The Times Top 100 Graduate Employers are featured in the 'Employer Entries' section of the directory. These entries describe what each organisation does, the opportunities they offer graduates, and practical details about their recruitment programme for 2003-2004.

The 'Employer Entry' section begins on page 27.

Each entry follows a standard format, and contains two elements: descriptive text and easy-to-find information on the employer's vacancies, contact details and salary expectations.

Locations of jobs
The regional locations of the employer's jobs are highlighted in red

Vacancies
The number of likely graduate vacancies at this employer in 2003-2004

Employer's graduate recruitment website address

Universities that the employer intends to visit
Most employers will be visiting a selection of UK universities during their recruitment programme. This gives you an indication of where they are intending to visit during 2003-2004.
You should always check with your careers service or the employer's website to see if the employer will be attending the careers fair or holding a presentation at your university.

Application deadline
Each employer has a different recruitment timetable and it is crucial that you apply at the right time. This part of their entry tells you whether they have a specific deadline or whether they accept applications throughout the year.

Contact Details
If the employer has a dedicated graduate recruitment telephone hotline or enquiries email address, you'll find it here.
Remember that you can request more information on all the employers in the book by completing the Information Request card on page 160.

General information about the employer

Career areas recruited for
Details of the generic career areas that the employer recruits for. There are sixteen areas to look out for:

- Accountancy
- Consultancy
- Engineering
- Finance
- General Management
- Human Resources
- Investment Banking
- IT
- Law
- Logistics
- Marketing
- Media
- Purchasing
- Research & Development
- Retailing
- Sales

Getting the Right Job with the Right Employer

by Alex Snelling
HR Manager, L'Oréal

Doing a degree is a great chance to spend three or four years studying something that you really enjoy, something that you are really passionate about. But it will also be the springboard to your career as a graduate and life after university, if you can match your experiences and interests to the right employment opportunities.

There is a huge range of resources available to help you with job hunting and, as a starting point, your local university careers service can't be recommended highly enough. They have a wealth of research material that can help you explore the kind of careers that might interest you and which areas you'll be suited to. Even if you're still in your first or second year then start early and get to know your careers service now!

If you know you have a vocation or a real interest in a particular type of work then this process is going to be much easier. Being drawn to teaching or having a lifelong obsession with cars or CD players at least points you in a certain direction. If you really have no idea what you'd like to do after university then speaking with a careers adviser can set you thinking about how your skills might translate into different employment areas.

You can also examine your time at university for pointers. If you're always producing the posters for your university society then maybe you enjoy communicating with people. Or perhaps you were the person who was good at dealing with awkward customers in your part-time job. No matter how little work experience you've done, each of your different life experiences can help you focus on who you are and what you see yourself doing when you start work.

At this stage it's important to think as broadly as possible and not to be constrained by your degree subject. Except for a few niche areas and the more obvious vocations such as engineering or scientific research, the majority of first jobs are open to graduates from any degree background. Just because you've studied an arts degree doesn't mean you can't apply for a sales or an IT management position – most employers will offer all the necessary training to enable you to take on new or unfamiliar roles, provided you have the right aptitude and enthusiasm for the work.

Once you have begun to home in on the career sectors that interest you, then the next step is to identify the employers recruiting graduates in those areas. Many major graduate employers produce brochures describing their recruitment, which you can pick up at your careers service. The internet can also be a big help here and is a great way to gather information about individual organisations. Alongside the big 'household name' recruiters, don't overlook the opportunities provided by small- and medium-sized enterprises and the public sector. Whilst these organisations may not be as obvious as the big names, they can offer exciting and worthwhile opportunities.

You can visit one of the 'graduate recruitment farms' such as Milkround.com or GTI's DoctorJob.com – websites that list information for a wide range of different graduate employers which is searchable by job function or industry – or you can log on directly to an employer's own website and click through to the recruitment section. Either way, this will give you a variety of useful details about employers and their opportunities – everything from their minimum entry requirements, their training programmes for new graduates, the recruitment and selection process, and often case studies of recent graduates.

All of this information is essentially what the employers want you to read, and although it is very helpful for comparing what's on offer, it's also important to balance it with other sources to give you a more complete picture. Many of the major newspapers have story archives which are searchable by company name – try this for some of the organisations that you are interested in and you may well find information that the recruiters didn't want you to see, such as poor financial results, redundancy programmes or lost contracts.

This may also be a good time to do some networking. If you have friends who graduated last year or have had work experience with any of the employers you are considering, ask them for their impressions – you're bound to get a different perspective from the brochure or recruitment website information.

By now, you may well have the makings of a shortlist of employers that you are thinking of applying to. The real test comes though when you meet with the organisations in person at one of their campus events. Many recruiters attend careers fairs or hold presentations at their target universities during the autumn and this is a golden opportunity to see how your perception of the company compares with the reality. Do their recruitment staff inspire you? Are their recent graduates the kind of people you could imagine working with?

Remember that when you meet companies at a fair or presentation, the representatives you're talking to could be agency staff who are just paid to hand out brochures, or it could be the HR Director. Don't waste time asking recruiters the obvious, like "do you have any jobs in marketing?" – that kind of information is on their website and they won't take you seriously. Making the right impression by dressing properly, posing intelligent questions and carrying a copy of your CV might make all the difference if you do run into a senior recruiter at an event.

Once you've formed your final impressions of the employers that you're interested in, all that remains is to prepare your applications. There is no magic formula for how many applications you need to make to be successful, but it's a time consuming process, so it's unlikely you'll be able to submit more than a dozen.

Many employers now use online recruitment systems and it is essential that you visit their website and explore the application form before you start filling it in. Most require a balance of biographical data about your education and longer, open-ended questions about your experiences and achievements. It's well worth going along to a CV workshop at your careers service to help you organise and arrange the information that you'll be using on the application forms.

Recruiters are generally looking for evidence from your time at university and other life experiences that will help them predict how you will perform when you start work. You'll need to include examples of when you've shown initiative, leadership, team working and a range of other competencies. This might come from instances during work experience you've had, any positions of responsibility you've held at university, or extra-curricular activities such as independent travel or overseas expeditions.

It's essential to answer the questions that each employer asks as accurately and directly as possible, ensuring you use clear and relevant examples. It's also important to make sure that the context of your examples is appropriate for the kind of job that you've applied to. If you want a job in financial management then make sure you refer to "the time I did the finances for the Law Society ball" or your charity fundraising activities at school.

On a practical level, take note of employers' application deadlines – they are all different and some can be quite early in the year – and take

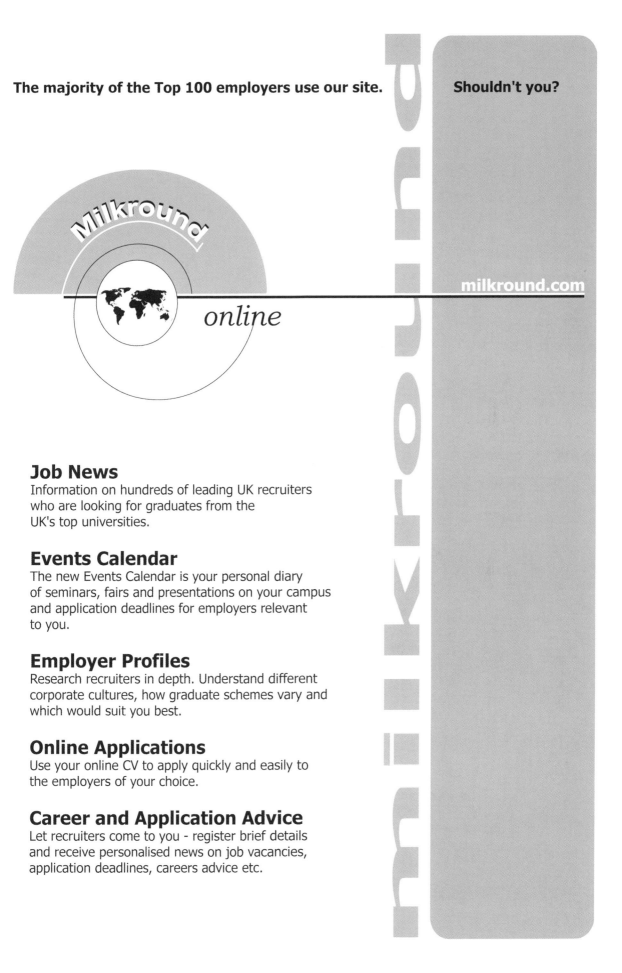

The majority of the Top 100 employers use our site.

Shouldn't you?

milkround.com

Job News
Information on hundreds of leading UK recruiters
who are looking for graduates from the
UK's top universities.

Events Calendar
The new Events Calendar is your personal diary
of seminars, fairs and presentations on your campus
and application deadlines for employers relevant
to you.

Employer Profiles
Research recruiters in depth. Understand different
corporate cultures, how graduate schemes vary and
which would suit you best.

Online Applications
Use your online CV to apply quickly and easily to
the employers of your choice.

Career and Application Advice
Let recruiters come to you - register brief details
and receive personalised news on job vacancies,
application deadlines, careers advice etc.

great care when you actually fill in your responses on- or off-line. Technology has moved on a lot but there are certain very traditional mistakes for which you will be heavily penalised – things like not changing the company name in a mail merged covering letter. Writing to L'Oréal and talking about how excited you are about career opportunities at Unilever is a real no-no. Equally, spelling mistakes, not using proper capitalisation or using abbreviations is a real indicator of a lack of attention to detail – would you really consider putting a candidate like this in charge of part of your business?

If your application is successful and you get a letter or email back from the company inviting you for interview then that's the point to take a step back and be very, very pleased – only a small number of applicants make it through to this stage.

The interview will develop and build on the information you've given in your original application. It's an exciting opportunity but isn't something to be nervous or tense about. Sensible preparations such as revisiting your company research, re-reading the website and brochure, and maybe going through a practice interview can help keep you calm on the day.

The final selection round is often an assessment centre, which can last up to two days or more. This is designed to give you the chance to show off your full range of skills and may well include tests, group exercises and more interviews. They are hard work, in-depth assessments but provide candidates with every opportunity to perform to the best of their ability.

The right job with the right employer should offer you much more than just a generous starting salary. Think through the training and development offer, the company culture and your future career prospects – don't be blinded by money because you could sell yourself very short in the long run.

Finally, persist. A recent candidate told the story of how they bought a special paper spike and impaled their rejection letters upon it. When they got their job, they had a bonfire! Keep a positive attitude and keep on applying until you secure your dream job.

Tips & Advice

- **Start as early as possible**
  Visit your careers service as soon as you can – it's the best place to start researching your job hunting as they've a wealth of material at your disposal.

- **Think about your interests**
  What do you like doing? Are you a born communicator or a natural salesperson? If you've had work experience, what did you enjoy most about it?

- **Keep an open mind**
  Just because you're studying a humanities course, you shouldn't rule out technical or commercial jobs – and vice versa.

- **Do your research**
  Use the internet and company brochures to find out all about your target employers.

- **Dig a bit deeper**
  Try and find out if there's anything that the employer might not want you to know – speak to friends and look on the web.

- **Go and meet them**
  Make the most of chatting to employers at a careers fair or campus presentation.

- **Consider the whole package**
  It's not all about money – look at everything that's on offer, such as the training & development.

- **Finally, do yourself justice**
  Take as much time as you can over the application form. Include relevant information that paints you in the best light and fits the employer's requirements. Your local careers service can give you valuable guidance on this.

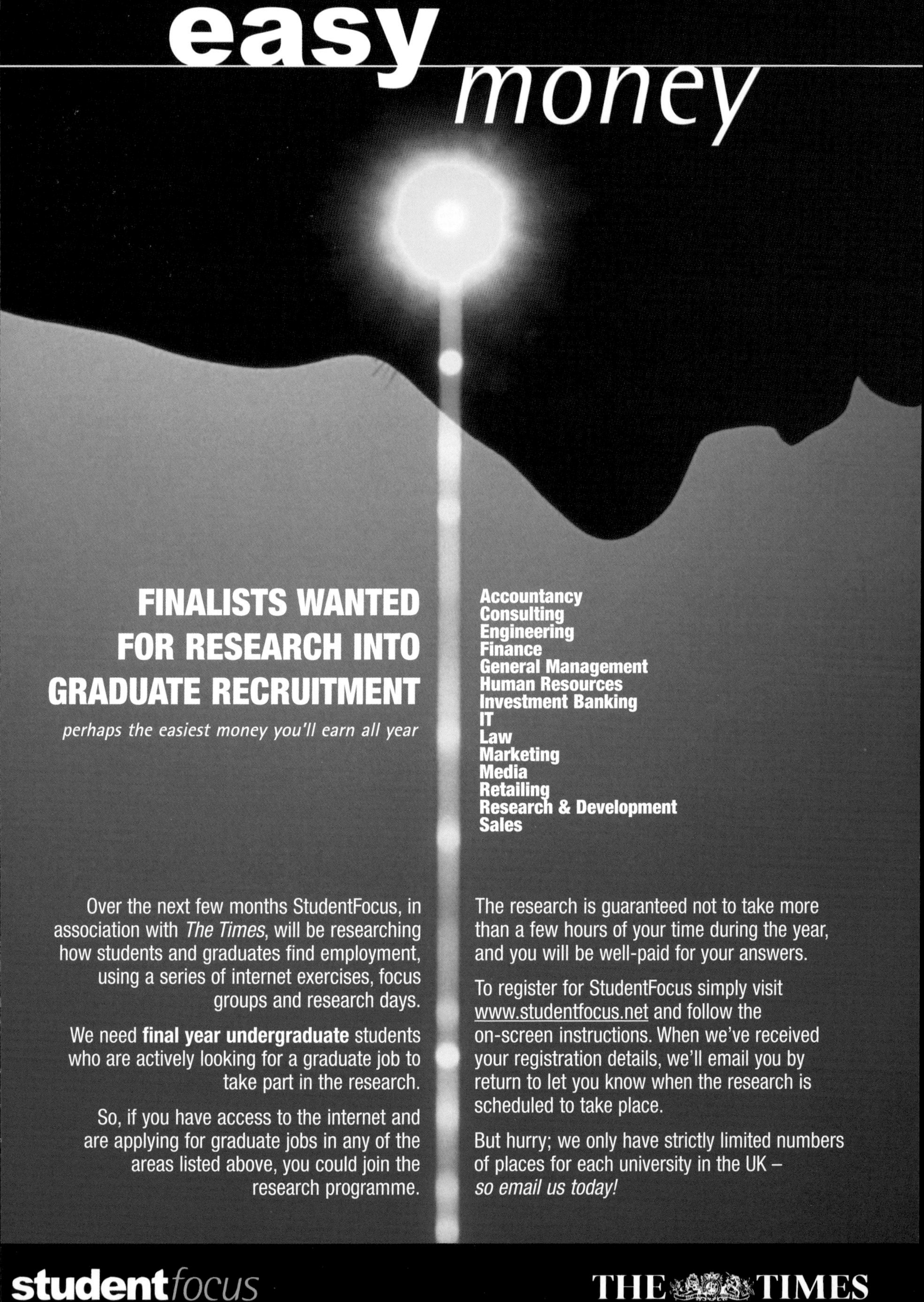

easy *money*

FINALISTS WANTED FOR RESEARCH INTO GRADUATE RECRUITMENT

perhaps the easiest money you'll earn all year

Accountancy
Consulting
Engineering
Finance
General Management
Human Resources
Investment Banking
IT
Law
Marketing
Media
Retailing
Research & Development
Sales

Over the next few months StudentFocus, in association with *The Times*, will be researching how students and graduates find employment, using a series of internet exercises, focus groups and research days.

We need **final year undergraduate** students who are actively looking for a graduate job to take part in the research.

So, if you have access to the internet and are applying for graduate jobs in any of the areas listed above, you could join the research programme.

The research is guaranteed not to take more than a few hours of your time during the year, and you will be well-paid for your answers.

To register for StudentFocus simply visit www.studentfocus.net and follow the on-screen instructions. When we've received your registration details, we'll email you by return to let you know when the research is scheduled to take place.

But hurry; we only have strictly limited numbers of places for each university in the UK – *so email us today!*

student *focus*

THE TIMES

Making the most of your University Careers Service

by Anne-Marie Martin
Director, University of London Careers Service

It's one of the great mysteries of higher education – many students go to university because they want a better job, but whilst they are there they do absolutely nothing at all about trying to get one.

In an environment where the degree is everything, it can be all-too-easy not to spend enough time on career management. Of course, it is important to strike a balance between the time you spend job-hunting and studying. Regardless of what employers say, you've got the rest of your life to find a job, but only three or four years to get a degree. On the other hand many students choose to shut out the process completely, then visit their careers service two weeks before graduation crying, "I need a job and I need it now". Finding your dream job takes time but fore-warned is definitely fore-armed. If you start thinking early enough, say in your second year, by the time you reach the study-packed final year you will have it sorted.

You see, to be successful you need to be able to convince an employer that you have an idea about your skills and abilities, strengths and weaknesses and a basic understanding of the relevant job market. Some clues about how best to penetrate the market and to sell yourself through the selection process will also help. None of this is rocket science; a little reflection at the end of each term is really all that is needed.

Although choosing a career and getting a job is something that you must ultimately do for yourself, your careers service is there to help identify where you are in the process and to help you succeed. Unfortunately, it's not quite as simple as being given the name of a particular occupation or organisation and being told, "apply here". At the end of the day it has to be your choice, because it's you that's going to do the job. However, your careers service is packed with products and services to help with every stage of the process including that all-too-tricky decision-making. You'd be astonished at how many different ways we can help you to start thinking about your options.

Different approaches work for different people, so your friend's experience of careers services may not be yours. Some people respond extremely well to talking to an individual adviser, some prefer the security of a group session, and others the anonymity of a computer programme or the time for consideration that written information provides. Some students have no idea what they want to do, whilst others are clear about their aspirations. The careers service can help the former with ideas and the latter with a check on whether their aspirations are realistic, perhaps clarifying what they need to do to ensure they achieve their goal.

It sounds daunting, but it really isn't. On your first visit to your careers service you'll probably be given an introduction to its facilities and the plethora of products and services at your disposal. These will include generic information about occupational areas and specific details on particular employers, as well as schedules of all the different activities, such as skills seminars and workshops, information and recruitment fairs and employer fora. Seminars can help you develop skills like working in a team or presenting to an audience. Checking CVs in a group situation can be very useful in helping you to appreciate the impact your resume has on other people. Careers services are in touch with the graduate labour market and know what jobs students from your subject entered last year and of course they provide access to vacancies, both temporary and permanent.

As your job-hunt progresses, most careers services will offer mock interview sessions, either with careers advisers or with employers who give feedback on your interview technique. Activities such as these can be incredibly useful – it's surprising how many of us can make pretty fundamental mistakes by not understanding the interviewing process.

Many students don't realise that careers services are quite happy to help with the early stages of your first permanent job, which can be very alien, such as how to behave in the working environment, or the formalities of contracts. Furthermore, your careers advisers don't stop being there for you once you've gained a job and graduated. The majority will offer some kind of support once you've left the institution. You may have to pay for these resources after university so why on earth not take advantage of them for free whilst you're a student?

Remember that your careers adviser will be happy to see you at any stage, from Freshers' week to your final year, whether you're advanced in your job hunt or whether you just want to touch base with them and discuss your ambitions. Despite constant reminders there will always be some students who fail to check the closing dates for graduate schemes or leave it too late to check on the experience required. It can be a huge shock to discover that, for example, city-based employers want you to have done some kind of relevant work in your second year vacation. Discovering that in your final year is not much help. You don't even need to pluck up the courage to meet your careers adviser physically – there are heaps of less threatening ways to interact with your service.

For example, many institutions offer an email registration service where you can be sent information about vacancies and events tailored to the kinds of job areas you specify – a great resource that really shouldn't be missed. Or perhaps your adviser might come to you, presenting a careers education session in your department; then you might register for a virtual careers interview or a seminar, and before you know it you've crossed the threshold into the service without ever actually speaking to an adviser. Alternatively, you can always just go and see them!

Red hot business leaders?

The ACA qualification

If you're planning to become one of tomorrow's red hot business leaders, start by following the path taken by around 3,000 of the sharpest young minds every year. The ACA qualification from the Institute of Chartered Accountants in England & Wales, is the number one financially based business qualification and can lead to a whole host of exciting, demanding and rewarding careers.

To begin exploring the world of colour opened up by the ACA, go to **www.icaew.co.uk/careers**, email **careers@icaew.co.uk** or call **01908 248040**

The full spectrum without the grey

THE ![crest] TIMES

TOP 100

GRADUATE EMPLOYERS

ABN·AMRO

Vacancies for around 50 graduates in 2004

- Accountancy
- Finance
- Investment Banking
- IT

Starting salary for 2004
£Competitive

Universities ABN AMRO plans to visit in 2003-4
Bath, Bristol, Cambridge, Edinburgh, Oxford, Reading, Warwick
Please check with your university careers service for details of events.

Application deadline
24th November 2003

Contact Details
graduaterecruitment@
uk.abnamro.com

Turn to Page 160 now to request more information about ABN AMRO.

ABN AMRO is one of Europe's leading international banking groups, with over 20,000 employees in nearly 50 countries, and current revenues of over €5 billion. The Wholesale Client Services arm is one of the largest investment and corporate banking businesses based in Europe today.

The Graduate Development Programme offers opportunities within specific business areas: Corporate Finance, Equities, Financial Markets, Client Relationship Management, Finance and Technology.

This comprehensive 12-month programme combines industry simulations, technical instruction, business-specific training and on-the-job coaching with regular feedback and dedicated support. The ABN AMRO Academy in Amsterdam provides graduates with leading edge development tools throughout their careers, as well as a vital exchange for establishing a network of contacts for the future. ABN AMRO's well-rounded scheme is geared to give graduates early responsibility, and to equip them with the skills and knowledge necessary to make a meaningful contribution from day one.

Graduates are selected for their tenacity and teamworking ability as well as their intellect and ambition. The required entrepreneurial instinct includes the confidence to act on ideas and build strong relationships with clients and colleagues alike. Naturally, a keen interest in the dynamics of banking and international finance will be essential.

A strong ethic of mutual support and co-operation runs through the business, and graduates at ABN AMRO will find an extensive network of people with advice and guidance to offer.

There is no bigger picture

Keep your focus wide

For real breadth of opportunity in corporate and investment banking, look no further than ABN AMRO.

To find out more about our Graduate Development Programme, please visit our website at:

www.graduate.abnamro.com

Keep your focus wide. Because there is no bigger picture than your future.

Deadline for completed applications: **24th November 2003.**

accenture

Innovation delivered.

www.accenture.com/ukgraduates

Vacancies for around 400 **graduates in 2004**

■ Consulting

■ IT

Starting salary for 2004
£Competitive

Universities Accenture plans to visit in 2003-4
Aston, Bath, Birmingham, Bristol, Cambridge, Durham, Edinburgh, Glasgow, Heriot-Watt, Leeds, London, Loughborough, Manchester, Newcastle, Nottingham, Oxford, Sheffield, Southampton, Strathclyde, UMIST, Warwick
Please check with your university careers service for details of events.

Application deadline
Rolling Recruitment

Contact Details
 ukgraduates@accenture.com
☎ 0500 100 189
Turn to Page 160 now to request more information about Accenture.

With over 75,000 people working in 47 countries, Accenture is a truly global management consulting and technology services organisation.

Their work invariably involves the application of information technology to business challenges. They implemented a regulatory news service for the London Stock Exchange and built the global diamond tracking system for De Beers. The projects vary, but it's always about the delivery of innovation.

There is a surprisingly close-knit feel to working at Accenture. Graduates control their own development and promotion is based entirely on the contribution they make. Flexible working programs allow for individuals to manage their own schedule, and Accenture also supports a range of charity programmes for those who want to give something back to their communities.

Graduates usually join as Analysts on the Professional Development Programme. In the first few weeks, technical training provides a solid grounding in the use and application of IT before graduates begin their first project, probably based at a client site. Specific activities vary, but for Analysts will typically include things like process analysis, testing and problem solving.

Accenture looks for more than just excellent academics. They need individuals who are passionate about something outside their studies, who have some work experience and an interest in business and technology.

Accenture is also pioneering a new career stream for technologists who would prefer to build deep technical skills. For information on this career path, please see their website at www.accenturetechnologysolutions.com/uk

Wendy Owen
University of Bath
International Management
and Modern Languages (French)

> accenture

nnovation delivered.

"I started at Accenture in January 2002, and went straight onto a training course. It was pretty daunting as a key part of what we were doing was computer coding and I had absolutely no experience of this. But once I realised we needed to think about the principles behind coding rather than the intricacies of it, I felt better and everyone was really helpful.

The projects I've worked on since then tend to blend technology and human performance, and I'm really enjoying this combination. My first project was with a chemicals company, managing their internal communications as they rolled out SAP. Right now, I'm working on a project for a major utilities company – we're helping them improve their customer relationship management by introducing new systems. My role has been to develop training materials. The people on my project come from 18 different countries, so it's a pretty varied bunch. There's a really relaxed working attitude and we socialise a lot together, often taking the clients out with us too.

Accenture do care about you having a life outside of work. There are so many clubs, and generally so much going on, it's almost like being back at university. Recently, I've been back to my old university, talking to other people about what it's like at Accenture, particularly those who are put off by the idea of working with technology. I'm proof that you don't have to be a techie to get on!"

Apply now at **www.accenture.com/ukgraduates**

• Consulting • Technology • Outsourcing • Alliances

AIRBUS

Vacancies for around
40-50 **graduates in 2004**

- Engineering
- Finance
- Human Resources
- Logistics

Starting salary for 2004
£19,500-£22,000

**Universities Airbus
plans to visit in 2003-4**
Bath, Bristol, London,
Loughborough, Nottingham,
Southampton, UMIST.
Please check with your university
careers service for details of events.

Application deadline
30th January 2004
See website for further details

Contact Details

[ ] airbusuk-grad@airbus.com

Turn to Page 160 now to request
more information about Airbus.

In just thirty years, Airbus has transformed the civil aviation industry, and now offers the most modern and comprehensive family of airliners currently on the market. It has delivered over 3,100 aircraft to more than 180 customers world-wide and boasts a healthy order book for delivery over the coming years.

Production began last year on the latest Airbus aircraft – the 555 seat A380 double-deck aircraft. Utilising the very latest technologies whilst keeping operating costs low and passenger comfort at an optimum, the A380 is truly an aircraft for the 21st Century. Airbus needs technically capable people who want to work for a company that offers world-class opportunities and expects world-class performance. Whilst most opportunities are to be found within the Design Engineering and Manufacturing areas, there are also a small number of additional opportunities based at both UK operating sites.

The Direct Entry Graduate Scheme offers a number of training placements throughout the first two years. These are carried out at the two UK sites and sometimes with strategic partners. Support is also offered in gaining professional accreditation where this is appropriate. Personal development is important and a development framework is in place. Graduates are encouraged to participate in off-the-job development such as community involvement projects.

Finally there is an attractive financial package with regular performance based reviews. Airbus is a truly multi-cultural and international organisation that offers varied and exciting career prospects.

To find out more, visit their website, www.airbus.com.

ALDI

Vacancies for unlimited
graduates in 2004

Retailing

Starting salary for 2004
£35,000
Rising to £50,000

**Universities that Aldi
plans to visit in 2003-4**
Please check with your university
careers service for details of events.

Application deadline
Rolling Recruitment
Applying early is strongly
recommended.

Contact Details

✉ recruitment@
aldi-stores.co.uk

Turn to Page 160 now to request
more information about Aldi.

In today's changing and challenging retail environment, Aldi
stands apart from the rest due to its unique style of operation
and innovative management system.

With over 5,000 stores across Europe, the US and Australia, the group is now
recognised as a world leader in grocery retailing. Aldi offers a range of
own-brand products of the highest quality at exceptionally low prices. The
structure of their range allows for a highly effective buying strategy and
incredibly cost-efficient retail system.

The 12-month training programme is dedicated to developing graduates'
knowledge and ability for the role of area manager. This demanding part of
their career will ensure they achieve their full potential. The programme covers
the structural and procedural elements of retail management, from store
operations and trading to administration, logistics and property.

The training commences in-store where graduates will take over the role of
store manager for several months. This hands-on experience is essential in
understanding Aldi's operation and the expectations on our people. The
second part of the training focuses on the role and responsibilities of the area
manager. During this time graduates will work alongside experienced
colleagues and oversee all aspects of the role including recruitment, planning
and organisation of the stores.

The career path beyond area management is challenging, and again well
rewarded. All senior management are recruited from within the company, and
successful area managers will have the opportunity to become a director,
reporting to the managing director of a region, or the group buying director.

come and meet the company

area managers
£35k + fully expensed Audi A4 rising to £50k + pension
Locations throughout the UK

The Company
Food retailer with 5,000 stores throughout mainland Europe, USA, UK, Australia and Ireland.

The Philosophy
To offer the customer a carefully selected range of high quality exclusive own label brands at heavily discounted prices.

The Concept
Unique, simple and effective.

The Vital Component
Our people.

The Opportunity
Area Management.

The Rewards
Top salary, empowerment, people management, responsibility.

The Qualities
Energy, determination, confidence, leadership. Graduated in last 7 years with a degree in any discipline.

The Responsibility
Your own group of stores, after 12 months training for the role.

The Potential
Director with special responsibilities within 5 years.

Confident that you've got what it takes? Then we would like to meet you.

Send a comprehensive CV (quoting ref UCLS) with a covering statement highlighting your leadership potential and indicating your preferred location, for example NW, SE etc, to :

Area Management Recruitment, ALDI GmbH & Co KG, Sheepcotes, Springfield Business Park, Chelmsford, Essex CM2 5AS.

Or apply online.

Visit us at www.aldi.com

Aldi is an equal opportunities employer

ALLEN & OVERY

www.allenovery.com

**Vacancies for around
120 graduates**
For training contracts commencing
September 2006 / March 2007

 Law

Starting salary for 2004
£28,500

**Universities Allen & Overy
plan to visit in 2003-4**
Birmingham, Bristol,
Cambridge, Cardiff, Durham,
Edinburgh, Exeter, Leeds,
Leicester, London,
Manchester, Newcastle,
Nottingham, Oxford, Sheffield,
Southampton, Warwick
**Please check with your university
careers service for details of events.**

Application deadline
See website for further details

Contact Details

✉ **graduate.recruitment@
allenovery.com**

☎ **020 7330 3000**
ask for Graduate Recruitment

Turn to Page 160 now to request
more information on Allen & Overy

Allen & Overy is a premier international law firm with over 4,800 people in 26 major centres worldwide. The firm's client list includes many of the world's top businesses, financial institutions, governments and private individuals.

Core practice areas are corporate, banking and international markets and the firm also has major strengths in other areas, including employment, pensions and incentives, litigation and real estate.

For Allen & Overy, today's trainees are tomorrow's leaders. The firm requires applicants with an excellent academic background, a genuine enthusiasm for the law, and both energy and initiative. Business awareness and an international perspective are prerequisite. The ability to work closely with others is also vital.

Flexibility and quality are hallmarks of their award-winning training. All trainees spend at least 12 months in core transactional practice areas and a minimum of three months gaining contentious experience, usually in the litigation department. Continual monitoring of agreed seat plans and assessment of progress ensure highly relevant and focused training. There are also opportunities for trainees to spend six months in one of their international offices. There are extremely high retention rates on qualification and the firm has a specialist Career Development Team which ensures that fee-earners and support staff receive the best professional training throughout their career with Allen & Overy.

By 2006 Allen & Overy will be based in new offices, shown above, in Bishops Square near Liverpool Street, as well as their office space in Canary Wharf.

ALLEN & OVERY

From day one **to one day...**

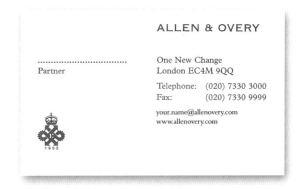

Every journey starts with the first step.

A training contract at Allen & Overy means your first steps to a legal career are with one of the world's leading law firms. If you are ambitious, energetic and passionate about the law, you could become one of our trainees for 2005/06, enjoying an award-winning training programme, supportive and comprehensive career development and an enviable culture of commitment, intellect and fun.

This will mean learning from some of the profession's foremost lawyers. It will mean working with leading clients on major cases as part of a focused and successful team. It will mean thinking like a lawyer as you develop into one. But most importantly, it will mean doing all this right from the start, not years down the line.

If you would like to find out more about training contracts, vacation placements and other important information such as deadlines, please contact:

graduate.recruitment@allenovery.com
Tel: 020 7330 3000

www.allenovery.com

▲ Arcadia Group Limited

Vacancies for around 150 graduates in 2004

- Finance
- Logistics
- Purchasing
- Retailing

Starting salary for 2004
£15,900-£19,500

Universities that Arcadia plans to visit in 2003-4
Cardiff, Dublin, Edinburgh, Kent, Leeds, Liverpool, London, Loughborough, Manchester, Newcastle, Nottingham Trent, Surrey, UMIST
Please check with your university careers service for details of events.

Application deadline
Rolling Recruitment
Applying early is strongly recommended. See website for further details.

Contact Details

✉ management.programmes@ arcadiagroup.co.uk

☎ 020 7927 1112

Turn to Page 160 now to request more information on Arcadia.

Arcadia Group is the UK's largest clothing retailer with over 25,000 employees, 2,000 outlets throughout the country and a growing number of international stores. The group includes eight celebrated High Street brands – Burton, Dorothy Perkins, Evans, Miss Selfridge, Outfit, Topshop, Topman and Wallis.

Arcadia has serious career opportunities for graduates who are passionate about their future. To help build on its impressive performance, the company is looking to recruit graduates with drive to succeed into the key areas of its operations – Retail Management, Finance, Distribution, Merchandising and Buying.

Whichever function graduates join, a programme of continuous learning will ensure that they enjoy a steady stream of new challenges and opportunities. At the same time they will benefit from formal courses focusing on specialist, personal and behavioural skills. The first 12 months will provide the foundation for a long-term career.

The Retail Management Programme commences with an intensive induction period. A structured framework of activities is designed to expose graduates to the broader retail picture, helping them to build up a network of contacts and support the individual's progression into Senior Store and Area Management.

Energy, leadership, commercial flair, initiative, customer focus and, above all, a passion for fashion are qualities that Arcadia prizes. In return graduates are given real responsibilities, structured training and development and the chance to have an impact on the business from day one.

Beautifully turned out careers...

...for graduates with a passion for fashion.

Arcadia is the name behind the leading High Street brands including, Burton, Dorothy Perkins, Evans, Outfit, Miss Selfridge, Topshop, Topman and Wallis.

Voted 'a leading Graduate employer in the Times Top 100' (the UK Graduate Careers Survey 2003), Arcadia has serious career opportunities for people who are passionate about their future.

www.arcadiagroup.co.uk/recruitment

Graduate Opportunities

- Retail Management
- Distribution/Allocation, Merchandising, Buying
- Finance
- 12 month Industrial Placements – for students studying a sandwich degree course

Rewards

You'll enjoy continuous training and development, a great benefits package including up to 25 days holiday, 25% discount on group merchandise, external discount offers, participation in the company bonus scheme and an excellent contributory pension scheme.

Apply Online today

Please check our website for the lastest job news and deadlines for applications.
Alternatively, speak to the Training Programmes Team on: 020 7927 1112.

▲ Arcadia Group Limited

We are committed to a policy of equal opportunities.

BURTON   DOROTHY PERKINS   Evans   ♡ Miss Selfridge   OUTFIT   TOPSHOP   **TOPMAN**   wallis

ARMY
BE THE BEST

www.armyofficer.co.uk

Vacancies for around 1,000 graduates in 2004

- Accountancy
- Engineering
- Finance
- General Management
- Human Resources
- IT
- Law
- Logistics

Please see the Army's website for a full list of officer careers

Vacancies also available elsewhere in the world

Starting salary for 2004
£24,247

Universities the Army plans to visit in 2003-4

Aberystwyth, Bath, Birmingham, Dundee, Edinburgh, Lancaster, Leeds, Liverpool, London, Loughborough, Manchester, Newcastle, Oxford, Plymouth, Sheffield

Please check with your university careers service for details of events.

Application deadline
Rolling Recruitment
Applying early is strongly recommended.

Contact Details

☎ 0845 600 1480

Turn to Page 160 now to request more information about the Army.

The British Army is regarded as one of the best and most professional organisations in the world. It retains this position largely because of the quality of its Officers and soldiers – ordinary young men and women who undertake some of the most challenging, yet rewarding tasks any job can offer.

The Army is especially interested in young people with engineering and technical degrees, but welcomes all graduates, because it offers such a diversity of jobs – from Engineer to Chaplain.

While a degree is important, of even greater importance are candidates' personal attributes. The Army provides exceptional careers for candidates with drive, self-confidence, a desire to lead, strong communication skills and who enjoy problem solving.

Army Officers receive managerial and leadership training that sets them up for a life-long career, whether in the Army or civilian life later on. Initial training takes place at the Royal Military Academy Sandhurst (RMAS) and covers all aspects of management and basic soldiering. Leadership abilities are developed so that young Officers can take responsibility for up to 50 soldiers. After RMAS, Officers join their Corps and undertake specialist training. Subsequently, they may study for Army-sponsored post-graduate or vocational qualifications.

Officers receive attractive pay and benefits, including free healthcare, non-contributory pension, six weeks paid holiday and subsidised living. In addition, there is access to sports and adventure training and a vibrant social life. To find out more about leading the best, visit www.armyofficer.co.uk.

ARMY OFFICERS ARE TRAINED TO OPEN DOORS MORE EASILY.

As an Army Officer, you're trained to do exceptional things.

To lead and manage under intense pressure. To make tough decisions in unfamiliar territory. To take responsibility for the people under your command, and the millions of pounds worth of equipment they operate.

These are skills that can take you a long way in your Army Career.

They'll also open an awful lot of doors for you afterwards.

For more information call 0845 600 1480 or visit www.armyofficer.co.uk

ARMY
BE THE BEST

part of the **WAL★MART** family

www.asda.com

Vacancies for around
85 graduates in 2004

Finance

General Management

IT

Logistics

Marketing

Purchasing

Retailing

Starting salary for 2004
£19,000

Universities that ASDA
plans to visit in 2003-4
Aberdeen, Birmingham,
Bristol, Cardiff, Durham,
Edinburgh, Glasgow,
Lancaster, Leeds, Liverpool,
Loughborough, Manchester,
Newcastle, Nottingham,
Strathclyde, Warwick, York
Please check with your university
careers service for details of events.

Application deadline
21st December 2003

Contact Details
Turn to Page 160 now to request
more information about ASDA.

ASDA was recently voted the UK's Best Employer 2003 by The Financial Times and one of the UK's top ten employers by The Sunday Times, an accolade achieved over the past three years. Part of the WAL-MART family, the world's most successful retailer, the entire business employs over 1.3 million worldwide.

Last year, global sales were more than $244 billion. In the UK they're the fastest growing retailer, employing 130,000 colleagues serving 8.5 million customers in 255 stores each week, supported by 24 distribution centres and ASDA House in Leeds. As a result, ASDA offers outstanding management and development opportunities, plus the chance to go global with WAL-MART.

Graduate vacancies exist in Retail Management, Buying, Trading and Supply, logistics, finance, George clothing and in the Information Systems Division.

ADSA's three year programme is designed to develop graduates to senior management in five years. From day one they are offered real responsibility, very quickly working up to management positions and working with £multi-million budgets. Opportunities after the three-year scheme also exist to relocate to America for 12 months on ASDA's International Leadership Development Programme, where managers can gain experience of working within the WAL-MART environment and culture, and in particular to develop retail skills by spending time working as a manager in a Wal*Mart store.

Minimum requirements are a 2.2 honours degree in any discipline, or a 2.1 honours degree in any discipline for finance. Retail Management graduates need to be mobile within a division of 50 stores, and logistics graduates need to be fully mobile nationwide.

"I've always wanted a career in retail, and after seeing the ASDA stand at a Careers Fair, I knew it was the company for me. Here was a business that promised to give me loads of responsibility, fast. And I can tell you, ASDA doesn't break its promises!

In just 6 years I've held seven positions across the organisation - from management roles such as Regional Trainer through to my present role as Games Buyer based at ASDA House. I'm responsible for buying in all our Playstation games, with a £multi-million budget that's a long way away from the money I had to spend as a student! It is hard work, I'm on the go all day, every day. But because I've set my sights on a more senior role, I'm happy to put in the hours. At ASDA, you get the freedom to do what you want and get where you want if you're prepared to go for it. I don't think you'd get the same opportunities anywhere else."

Raj Varma, age 30,
Games Buyer, ASDA House

"From a student loan to a £multi-million budget in just 5 years"

AstraZeneca

Vacancies for around 100 graduates in 2004

- Engineering
- Finance
- IT
- Logistics
- Marketing
- Purchasing
- Research & Development
- Sales

Starting salary for 2004
£Competitive

Universities AstraZeneca plan to visit in 2003-4
Please check with your university careers service or the AstraZeneca website for details of events.

Application deadline
Early December 2003

Contact Details
✉ info@ideas.astrazeneca.com
☎ 0800 073 0403
Turn to Page 160 now to request more information about AstraZeneca.

One of the world's leading pharmaceutical companies, AstraZeneca's success is based on turning innovative ideas into medicines which make a real difference to people's lives.

Backed by its strong research base and extensive manufacturing and commercial capabilities, the company provides an energising environment in which to develop graduates' careers.

More than just access to great courses and programmes, AstraZeneca can offer a supportive learning and development environment. After agreeing a personal plan with a graduate's manager, the company's people development framework provides them with the necessary resources to excel in their existing role and fulfill their long term career ambitions.

AstraZeneca supports a performance-based culture with competitive salaries and bonuses linked to employee's personal contribution and the company's overall performance. However, many believe it is AstraZeneca's benefits package that offers the real incentive; an extensive range of reward options offers unprecedented choice, value and flexibility.

AstraZeneca expects all its people to take responsibility for moving the company forward. Leadership, at all levels, is therefore key. A range of leadership and management development programmes are designed to help in this area, developing skills for today and supporting success for tomorrow.

Another benefit of joining AstraZeneca is that graduates will enjoy the support of the company's work/life balance initiatives and the potential for flexible working opportunities. Its largest sites enjoy an excellent range of social, cultural and sporting activities.

I want to be inspired.

A history of innovation. A passion for discovery. A culture that encourages you to explore new ideas. These are the qualities that make AstraZeneca different from most large organisations. And the ones that make it such an inspiring place to establish your career.

From day one, we think everyone can contribute. And that everyone can change the way we do things. We don't recruit graduates solely on the strength of past achievements, but rather on their potential and what we think they can achieve.

Whatever your degree and wherever you join us – the work you do here will have a positive impact on your own career and on the lives of other people. To find out more, visit our website www.ideas.astrazeneca.com

www.ideas.astrazeneca.com

AstraZeneca
life inspiring ideas

BAE SYSTEMS

Vacancies for around
300 graduates in 2004

- Engineering
- Finance
- General Management
- Human Resources
- IT
- Marketing
- Purchasing
- Research & Development

Starting salary for 2004
£21,000

Universities BAE SYSTEMS
lans to visit in 2003-4

Bath, Birmingham, Bristol,
Brunel, Edinburgh, Glasgow,
Heriot-Watt, Lancaster,
Leeds, Liverpool,
Loughborough, Manchester,
Nottingham, Plymouth,
Sheffield, Southampton,
UMIST, Warwick
Please check with your university
careers service for details of events.

Application deadline
Rolling Recruitment
Applying early is strongly
recommended

Contact Details

☎ 01772 677 277

Turn to Page 160 now to request
more information about
BAE SYSTEMS.

In the exciting arena of international aerospace and defence,
BAE SYSTEMS is a leading player with a wealth of opportunities.

Their business extends globally with a range of programmes in the land, sea
and air sectors. The company recognise that no two people are alike and aim
to offer a range of career paths which appeal to a broad range of individuals.

BAE SYSTEMS' graduate development framework has long been held as one
of the best available. In their drive to continuously improve, BAE SYSTEMS are
looking to further develop their graduate development programmes for 2004.
The revised programmes will continue to offer a combination of personal,
management and functional development courses.

While BAE SYSTEMS offers a wide range of opportunities for development,
they recognise that graduates are responsible for driving their own
development at a pace which suits them. Graduates will be supported in this
by their manager and mentor. Where appropriate, BAE SYSTEMS can support
graduates towards further professional qualifications.

BAE SYSTEMS have a large requirement for engineers, including aeronautical,
avionics, mechanical, electrical, electronics, manufacturing, software and
systems engineers. On the business side, they need high-calibre graduates to
become professionals in finance, procurement, commerce and marketing.

They offer an excellent package, including a competitive salary with six
monthly performance reviews, an initial sign-up bonus, 25 days' holiday per
year and the opportunity to participate in share, healthcare and car lease
schemes. To find out more about the exciting opportunities available, or to
make an application, please visit www.graduates-baesystems.com

Where are we coming from?
Where are we going?

how
will it feel?

Look ahead. What do you want to be in five years' time? A respected specialist in your field? A high-performance manager? An influential international executive? With us, anything's possible.

BAE SYSTEMS is an internationally respected organisation. Our vision is to be the leading systems company, innovating for a safer world. How? By equipping international peacekeeping forces and enabling nations to protect their communities. With nearly 100,000 people located across five continents, we design, manufacture and support intelligent solutions from ingeniously small components to extraordinarily complex integrated information systems. How will you make your mark?

Through three carefully structured graduate programmes – GDF, FLDP and SIGMA – we can provide the training, support and direction you need to meet your ambitions. You just need to decide which route is right for you. To help you choose, please visit our website at www.graduates-baesystems.com where you will also find further information and an online application form. Alternatively, contact us on 01772 677 277 for a copy of our brochure. Then **start** anticipating.

At BAE SYSTEMS, we believe that a diverse workforce benefits us all. To achieve our vision to be the leading systems company, innovating for a safer world, we need to recruit and develop the best and the brightest, regardless of race, gender, age or background.

BAE SYSTEMS

BARCLAYS

www.careers.barclays.co.uk

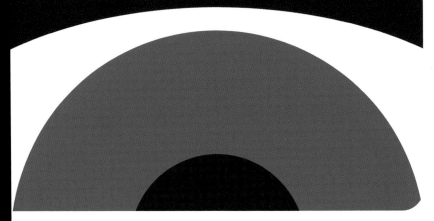

Look no further.

Vacancies for around 70 graduates in 2004

- Accountancy
- Finance
- Human Resources
- IT
- Marketing
- Sales

Vacancies also available in Europe

Starting salary in 2003
£22,500-£25,000
with a £3,000 joining bonus

Universities that Barclays plans to visit in 2003-4
Bath. Belfast. Birmingham.
Bristol. Brunel. Cambridge.
Durham. Lancaster. Leeds.
London. Manchester.
Nottingham. Oxford. Sheffield.
UMIST. Warwick
Please check with your university careers service for details of events.

Application deadline
Year-round recruitment
See website for further details

Contact Details
Turn to Page 160 now to request more information about Barclays.

Barclays offers much more than just high street banking for personal customers. It is also a leading provider of tailored and specialist financial services to high net worth clients, small and medium businesses, multinational corporations and financial institutions.

The size and diversity of the organisation ensures that for exceptional and driven individuals Barclays can offer a varied and challenging career path and provide them with the visibility and opportunity they need to develop their skills and demonstrate their ability.

Successful candidates will have the chance to become part of the Barclays future leadership team; supported by the organisation, they will gain unique experiences and insights imperative to the ongoing success of Barclays. Unafraid to instigate change and initiate new and better ways of doing things, recruits must also be highly committed to both the organisation and their own career path.

Graduates wishing to join will have a strong academic record and intellectual ability (ideally a minimum of 22 UCAS points and a 2.1 honours degree or international equivalent). They can think creatively and develop innovative solutions to problems. They will also demonstrate a belief in themselves and in their own values. Above all, individuals will be able to demonstrate commercial acumen and real experiences above and beyond their university education.

Barclays offers a challenging and dynamic working environment where people are expected and encouraged to challenge the status quo, suggest fresh and innovative ideas, and be held accountable for them.

High
visibility

Stand out.

www.barclays.co.uk/careers

Barclays is committed to equality of opportunity
and welcomes applications from all sections of the community.

BARCLAYS
FLUENT IN FINANCE

BDO Stoy Hayward

**Specialist advisers
to growing businesses**

**Vacancies for around
100 graduates in 2004**

Accountancy

**Starting salary for 2004
£Competitive**

**Universities that BDO
plans to visit in 2003-4**
Bath, Belfast, Birmingham,
Bristol, Cambridge, Durham,
Exeter, Leeds, Liverpool,
London, Loughborough,
Manchester, Nottingham,
Oxford, Reading, Sheffield,
Southampton, St Andrews,
Stirling, Strathclyde, Surrey,
Ulster, UMIST, Warwick
Please check with your university
careers service for details of events.

**Application deadline
Rolling Recruitment**
Applying early is strongly
recommended.

Contact Details

 graduate.recruitment@bdo.co.uk

☎ 020 7893 3009

Turn to Page 160 now to request more
information about BDO Stoy Hayward.

BDO Stoy Hayward is the world's fifth largest firm of chartered
accountants, providing a range of advisory services to
entrepreneurial businesses.

A mixture of ambition, drive and entrepreneurial flair has seen them establish
themselves as a major player in their field, particularly as specialist advisers to
growing businesses. In spite of a strong international presence, the firm has
retained a distinctly personal approach to their clients and graduates alike.
This results in early responsibility, recognition and scope for those who are
prepared to use their initiative.

They also take pride in promoting an environment that encourages individuality
and training is tailored to individual needs to reflect this. Employees have
access to training and development managers whose advice enables them to
take full advantage of the extensive programme of developmental courses
available.

Graduates are very much seen as the future of the business, so the firm makes
a strong commitment to career development. A high value is placed on forging
strong bonds both internally and with clients. They also provide superb support
towards achieving either the ACA, ACCA or ATT/CTA, but expect a high degree
of personal responsibility in return.

Applicants are required to have at least a 2.1 honours degree in any subject,
as well as a minimum of 22 UCAS points (280 on new tariff) or equivalent,
excluding General Studies.

For more information, please refer to the BDO Stoy Hayward brochure
and website.

You did.
I didn't.
You did.
I didn't.
You've been doing it for weeks.
That's rubbish, Claire.
Who the hell...

...is Claire?

You've got a perfectly good name. And we'll use it.

There's no mistaking the strength of BDO Stoy Hayward – now ranked as the fifth largest chartered accountancy firm in the world. But there is something that sets us apart from the other big hitters. We like to get closer to people. And that's true for clients and graduates alike. That's how we've established ourselves as specialist advisers to growing businesses. And that's why you can expect more responsibility and more recognition as one of our trainees.

We have openings in Audit and Business Advisory, General Business Tax, Specialist Tax and Business Recovery Services. Whichever area you choose, you will gain early integration into teams working with clients such as the Body Shop, Toni & Guy and the RSPCA. We'll also provide full training to build your business skills and support you towards achieving either the ACA, ACCA or ATT/CTA professional qualifications. So if you have entrepreneurial energy, a good head for figures and a 2:1 degree (achieved or expected) in any degree discipline, remember our name. You'll mean more to us. To find out how much more, please apply online at www.bdo.co.uk/graduate

Vacancies for around 85 graduates in 2004

- Accountancy
- Engineering
- General Management
- Human Resources
- Purchasing
- Research & Development

Starting salary for 2004
£20,000

Universities that BNFL plans to visit in 2003-4
Bath, Birmingham, Bristol,
Durham, Lancaster, Leeds,
Liverpool, Loughborough,
Manchester, Newcastle,
Sheffield, Strathclyde, UMIST
Please check with your university
careers service for details of events.

Application deadline
Rolling Recruitment
Applying early is strongly
recommended.

Contact Details
✉ graduates@bnfl.com
☎ 01946 786044
Call only if unable to access website

Turn to Page 160 now to request
more information about BNFL.

BNFL is an international nuclear energy business, serving Governments and nuclear utilities worldwide, operating in 16 countries and employing more than 23,000 people.

Safety is BNFL's number one priority and they recognise it is vital never to lose sight of their responsibilities to the environment, their workforce and the communities in which they work and live.

Each year they recruit graduates into engineering, science and commercial functions, offering exciting job opportunities that span the Operations, R&D, Design Engineering and Commercial spectrum. Their main locations are Cumbria, Cheshire, Lancashire and Gloucestershire.

Successful candidates join the two-year graduate development programme, ELEMENTS – their tailor-made graduate programme through which graduates develop their technical and professional skills and benefit from mentor and line manager support. BNFL's technical programmes are accredited by many institutes including the IEE, ICE, IChemE, IMechE, IOP, RSC and IOM. All graduates are encouraged to achieve chartered status.

Whichever career path a graduate embarks upon in BNFL, ELEMENTS provides an excellent technical and professional platform. Upon appointment, graduates are assigned to a real job with real responsibility and also participate in training development experiences to broaden their skills.

BNFL offer competitive benefits that include a starting salary of £20,000+, final salary pension scheme, generous vacation and a £1,500 welcome award. Their policy is to treat company employees and job applicants fairly, impartially and without prejudice on the basis of race, sex or disability.

developing graduates responsibly

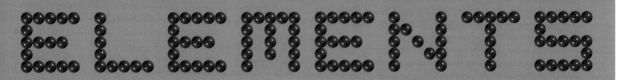

ELEMENTS

Science   Engineering   Commercial

www.bnfl.com

Apply online.

Vacancies for around
250 graduates in 2004

- Engineering
- Finance
- General Management
- Human Resources
- IT
- Marketing
- Purchasing
- Research & Development
- Sales

Vacancies also available in Europe

Starting salary in 2003
£18,500-£25,000

Universities that BT plans to visit in 2003-4
Aston, Bath, Belfast, Birmingham, Bristol, Brunel, Cambridge, Cardiff, Dublin, Durham, Edinburgh, Glasgow, Lancaster, Leeds, London, Loughborough, Manchester, Nottingham, Oxford, Sheffield, Southampton, St Andrews, Strathclyde, Surrey, UMIST, Warwick, York
Please check with your university careers service for details of events.

Application deadline
Please visit the BT website for deadline information.

Contact Details
Turn to Page 160 now to request more information about BT.

BT is one of Europe's leading providers of communications services. Its principal activities include local, national and international telecommunications services, higher-value broadband and internet products and services, and IT solutions.

In the UK, BT serves over 21 million corporate and residential customers with more than 28 million exchange lines, as well as providing network services to other licensed operators.

The company has opportunities ranging from highly specialised technical opportunities through to broad commercial roles. They are looking for graduates who have or expect a 2.1 honours degree or better and whose qualities fit with the clear objectives of the organisation. BT particularly welcomes candidates with relevant work experience and language skills. GCSE English Language and Maths at grade C or above is also required. BT positively encourages women, people from ethnic minorities and people with disabilities to apply and believes that nobody should face unfair discrimination.

Graduates will enjoy competitive starting salaries in line with market rates and their individual skills, experience and qualifications. Salaries are reviewed regularly. There is a comprehensive benefits package, including Sharesave and profit sharing schemes, interest free loans and the opportunity to join the BT Retirement Plan.

There is a comprehensive graduate development programme, opportunities to study for professional qualifications in some areas and access to a wealth of on-line training modules through the BT Academy, their on-line learning portal. Placement opportunities are also available for penultimate year students.

Do you have the potential to inspire the future of communication?

People have always found extraordinary ways of communicating with one another. At BT we're looking for ambitious, forward-thinking people who have the ability to help shape the way we communicate for generations to come. If you are seeking intellectual challenge, real responsibility and want to make a difference, then we want to hear from you.

Whether you're a graduate, undergraduate or interested in a modern apprenticeship, we've got lots of jobs across all areas and you'll find that a career with BT won't just shape your future, it could also shape everyone's.

Visit bt.com/careers

INVESTOR IN PEOPLE

BT is an equal opportunity employer

POSITIVE ABOUT DISABLED PEOPLE

More Connections. More Possibilities.

Cadbury Schweppes

Vacancies for around
15-20 graduates in 2004

Accountancy

Engineering

Finance

Human Resources

IT

Logistics

Marketing

Purchasing

Research & Development

Sales

Starting salary for 2004
£21,500-£25,000

Universities that Cadbury Schweppes plans to visit in 2003-4
Birmingham, Loughborough, Nottingham, Oxford, Warwick
Please check with your university careers service for details of events.

Application deadline
28th November 2003
See website for further details

Contact Details
Turn to Page 160 now to request more information about Cadbury Schweppes.

Cadbury Schweppes is a major international beverage and confectionery company, selling much-loved brands in over 200 countries worldwide.

Whether beavering away on product innovation at Bournville or boosting sales in Beijing, all 55,000+ Cadbury Schweppes people are united behind one core purpose: working together to create brands people love.

The name behind many a well-loved brand, Cadbury Schweppes is also a byword for commercial and personal integrity, where good values and good business go hand in hand. The result is a modern, forward-thinking company with a reputation for ongoing growth, great brands and progressive employment practices, and for being strong corporate citizens with a finger on the pulse of business performance and a focus on strong shareholder returns.

When it comes to graduate recruitment, they are looking for the best, regardless of discipline. A science whiz? A history buff? Exceptional graduates of all kinds will find Cadbury Schweppes the perfect place to develop their talents, broaden their experience and realise their ambitions.

Graduates will be given real responsibilities and opportunities from day one, underpinned by a development programme tailored to each individual and a highly collaborative way of working; within the first few years the chances are they will gain overseas experience. Add a competitive salary, support in studying for relevant professional qualifications, a diverse community of like-minded peers, great business units to work in and amazing brands to champion – all in all, it's an ideal springboard to an immensely rewarding and satisfying career, the start of a life changing experience.

Cadbury Schweppes

the place to be

At Cadbury Schweppes, we work together to create brands people love. Brands like Cadbury, Dr Pepper, Schweppes, Trebor, Halls, Orangina, Snapple and Bassett's that bring moments of delight to millions of people around the world. So how do we go about doing it? More than anything else, by recruiting great people and continuously improving their creativity, commitment and capabilities. If you have bags of talent, a track record to shout about and can bring a touch of magic to our company, we'd love to hear from you.

To find out more,
visit www.cadburyschweppes.com

CIVIL SERVICE
of Northern Ireland

Vacancies for graduates in 2004 are to be confirmed

■ **General Management**

Starting salary for 2004
£18,440
Under review

Universities that the Northern Ireland Civil Service plans to visit in 2003-4
Please check with your university careers service for details of events.

Application deadline
14th November 2003

Contact Details
Turn to Page 160 now to request more information about the Northern Ireland Civil Service.

Reshaping the education system, hospital reforms, transport and urban regeneration – these are some of the headline issues that make the Northern Ireland Civil Service (NICS) a challenging and rewarding place to work.

To deliver successfully on these and other major issues, NICS needs talented people who want to help shape the future for the people living and working in Northern Ireland today. NICS employs over 28,000 staff across its 11 departments and associated agencies. Whichever department or agency graduates join, you'll be helping to make a real difference to people's lives on all kinds of levels.

These opportunities afford graduates the chance to enter the NICS at middle management level (Staff Officer) with a competitive starting salary, generous annual leave (minimum 22 days plus statutory days), a generous pension scheme and flexible working hours in most locations. High quality training tailored to the individual together with a corporate induction programme to help new graduates become familiar with the NICS is also provided.

Joining the NICS means being part of a dynamic and fast-changing organisation. NICS came joint first in a UK wide survey conducted by the Work-Life Balance Trust for the publication 'The Graduate Guide', aimed at providing graduates with information to enable them to make a positive start in their hunt for a career.

These NICS graduate career opportunities, therefore, provide the appropriate mix of real challenge and responsibility, generous family friendly benefits and quality training.

I'm looking for a real challenge

Graduate
Career
Opportunities

Starting Salary: £18,440

Anything but ordinary

Think about the Northern Ireland Civil Service, think about...

- Shaping the future for people in Northern Ireland

- Tackling headline issues like reshaping the education system or reform of public services

- Working on complex challenges such as urban regeneration or investing in health initiatives

- Advising government ministers on major issues of the moment.

To find out more about the challenges we have to offer visit our website
www.nics.gov/recruitment

Applicants who want anything but the ordinary must hold, or have been awarded by 31 July 2004, a 2.1 honours degree or higher in any discipline, or an alternative formal qualification deemed equivalent by the NICS.

The Northern Ireland Civil Service is committed to equality of opportunity in employment. All applications for employment will be considered on the basis of merit. The Northern Ireland Civil Service welcomes applications from all suitably qualified candidates irrespective of religious belief, gender, disability, race, political opinion, age, marital status, sexual orientation or whether or not they have dependants.

CIVIL SERVICE
of Northern Ireland

www.nics.gov.uk/recruitment   think career, think...

CREDIT SUISSE | FIRST BOSTON

Vacancies for around 75-100 graduates in 2004
Full time Analyst positions. A further 85-100 Summer Analyst positions are available – check website for details.

■ Finance
■ Investment Banking
■ IT

Vacancies also available in Europe

Starting salary for 2004
£35,000-£40,000

Universities CSFB plans to visit in 2003-4
Bristol, Cambridge, London, Oxford, Warwick
Please check with your university careers service for details of events.

Application deadlines
14th November 2003
Full-time Analyst positions in Investment Banking, Equities & Fixed Income

5th December 2003
Full-time Technical Associate positions in Information Technology

30th January 2004
All Summer Internship positions

Contact Details
☎ 020 7883 5100
Turn to Page 160 now to request more information about CSFB.

CSFB is a leading global investment bank serving institutional, corporate, government and high net worth clients. Businesses include securities underwriting, sales and trading, investment banking, private equity, financial advisory services, venture capital, investment research and asset management.

CSFB's overarching objective is to build strong relationships with clients enabling them to capitalise fully on their broad capabilities and overall strength. Whether rapidly executing trades or developing long-range strategic financing plans, CSFB work in partnership with clients, finding solutions that realise maximum value in each unique situation.

As a full-time Analyst in Investment Banking, Equities or Fixed Income, graduates benefit from an induction programme lasting two to three months followed by a further two to three years of structured training. This includes presentations from senior managers, an overview of financial markets and in-depth role-related training. Within IT, the training programme starts with a three week induction to ease the transition from study to work. Graduates are then launched into their role with a further two weeks' tailored technical training followed by on-the-job training and coursework. Interns in these divisions also benefit from exposure to senior management and training in financial markets, together with the chance to interact with colleagues and fellow interns.

CSFB look for individuals who question, innovate, spot opportunities and look beyond the obvious. It's the ability to think creatively and responsibly, and to make things happen, that will add value to CSFB's clients and enable them to take advantage of change.

CREDIT SUISSE | FIRST BOSTON

NO GOING WITH THE FLOW. NO FORMULA.
NO RESTRICTED VIEW. NO ACCEPTED WISDOM.
NO ONE WAY.

www.csfb.com

Free thinkers have made us one of the world's leading investment banks. Which is why we look for graduates who, like us, question, innovate, spot opportunities and look beyond the obvious. These are essential qualities whichever one of our business areas you want to join – **Investment Banking, Fixed Income, Equities** or **Information Technology.** Naturally you'll be gifted academically. But it's your ability to think creatively and responsibly, and to make things happen, that will add value to our clients and enable them to take advantage of change. Your input will help fuel the momentum that will ultimately make us number one in our industry. If you'd like to find out about the different ways we can encourage your development, including our investment in your training, please click on www.csfb.com

CSFB | **EMPOWERING CHANGE.**

Deloitte

Vacancies for around 600 graduates in 2004

- Accountancy
- Consulting
- Finance
- IT

Starting salary for 2004
£Competitive

Universities Deloitte plans to visit in 2003-4

Bath, Birmingham, Bristol, Cambridge, Cardiff, Durham, Edinburgh, Exeter, Glasgow, Heriot-Watt, Leeds, London, Loughborough, Manchester, Newcastle, Nottingham, Oxford, Sheffield, Southampton, Strathclyde, UMIST, Warwick
Please check with your university careers service for details of events.

Application deadline
31st January 2004
First deadline.
Please see the Deloitte website for further deadline details.

Contact Details

✉ gradrec.uk@deloitte.co.uk

☎ 0800 323333

Turn to Page 160 now to request more information about Deloitte.

People still often refer to big 'accountancy' firms, but in today's world, the phrase just doesn't do justice to the breadth of work undertaken by Deloitte.

The firm talks instead of 'professional services' and offers a wide variety of services to their clients – recruiting graduates into careers that range from assurance and advisory work and corporate tax through to consultancy, actuarial advice and IT.

For those choosing to pursue a career in accountancy and tax, it's good to know that Deloitte has regularly outperformed its competitors in the ACA exams and consistently exceeded the ATT's overall national pass rates too. Whatever the role, the long-term career prospects are excellent, with a chance to take on early responsibility and, in certain roles, travel internationally too.

Every office and practice will have its own unique culture, of course, but many new joiners are struck by just how open and non-hierarchical the Deloitte business world really is. The firm's Partners are respected for their experience, expertise and judgement, but they are not remote figures who can never be approached. Open-plan offices encourage frank and straightforward communication between colleagues.

The people who comprise the graduate intake will provide much the same social network and mutual support that they found at university. Often, they become friends as well as colleagues. What's more, there is an impressive range of more organised sports and social activity that goes on within Deloitte, ranging from black tie events to regular five-a-side football fixtures.

"You're measuring yourself against the best."

Kirstine Otty, Literature graduate.

When you're working at Deloitte, you know that your colleagues are some of the highest achievers around. You also know, however, that there's plenty of support on offer to help you fulfil your true potential.

If you're interested in finding out more and starting a two-way conversation about the possibilities and potential that exist, simply visit our website, where you can find out how to apply.

Careers available:
- Chartered Accountancy
- Tax
- Consulting
- Advisory
- Actuarial
- IT

Academic criteria:
Varies by service line:
- A or B at Maths and English GCSE or equivalent
- 22-26 UCAS points or equivalent
- 2:1 or 2:2 degree

Locations:
- Nationwide

Stonecutter Court, 1 Stonecutter Street, London EC4 4TR.
Freephone: 0800 323333.

http://graduates.deloitte.co.uk

Deloitte & Touche LLP is an equal opportunities employer.

Deloitte

DIAGEO

www.diageo.com/graduates

Vacancies for around 30-40 graduates in 2004

- Engineering
- Finance
- General Management
- Human Resources
- IT
- Logistics
- Marketing
- Purchasing
- Research & Development
- Sales

Starting salary for 2004
£Competitive

Universities Diageo plans to visit in 2003-4
Aston, Bath, Belfast, Birmingham, Cambridge, Dublin, Durham, Edinburgh, Glasgow, London, Oxford, St Andrews, Strathclyde, Ulster, UMIST, Warwick
Please check with your university careers service for details of events.

Application deadline
31st December 2003

Contact Details
✉ graduates@diageo.com
☎ 0208 978 6000
Turn to Page 160 now to request more information about Diageo.

The people and the passion. Diageo is the world's leading premium drinks company with an unrivalled collection of brands. They are a young vibrant organisation, but the drinks they're associated with have a history that in some cases extends back several centuries – names like Smirnoff, Johnnie Walker, J&B Rare and Guinness are recognised and enjoyed by millions the world over.

But Diageo is not only about legendary brands. It's also about people – talented, passionate individuals who put their all into their work, yet always find time to enjoy life to the full.

Diageo believe in unleashing the creativity and enthusiasm of these people by handing them the opportunities that stretch them to the limit. It's only then that they experience the deep satisfaction of achieving something they thought was beyond their reach. It's only then that they embrace the new and the unknown, to become the very best they can possibly be.

The best way to appreciate what it's like to work at Diageo is to think of a culture in which people play hard, but work even harder. Everyone at the organisation is passionate about the brands they work with, but they never forget that they are a business, and an extremely successful one at that.

Regardless of the activity graduates are engaged in – be it in sales, marketing, finance, human resources, production, procurement, research & development or logistics – they will have big targets to hit. Achieving those goals is something that Diageo take extremely seriously.

DIAGEO

The world's leading premium drinks business

We were at the festival together

You sang, you laughed, you ate food your parents wouldn't recognise. You redefined the meaning of personal hygiene. You had an amazing time. With our portfolio of world-famous brands we were right there with you. And that'll go for your career too.

Diageo operates in 180 countries around the world, so your creativity and enthusiasm will be unleashed in an environment that really will stretch you to the limit. The ongoing success of our brands means we can offer you the opportunity to gain valuable experience in a wide range of functions from Sales & Marketing to Production & Logistics – and everywhere in between.

We're looking for talented graduates with the vision, the skills and the ambition to make the most of this opportunity right from day one. We want to create the business leaders of the future and will provide all the training you need to achieve your full potential.

You know who we are. Have you got what it takes to join us? Find out more at **www.diageo.com/graduates**

You know who we are. Be part of us.

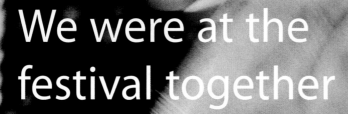

Since 1999, night time adventurers have enjoyed more than 2 billion ice cold bottles of Smirnoff Ice

SMIRNOFF ICE
VODKA MIXED DRINK

SMIRNOFF ICE

A blend of pure Smirnoff Red vodka with the classic taste of lemon
SERVE EXTRA CHILLED

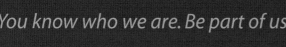

Vacancies for around 85 graduates

For training contracts commencing in 2006

■ Law

Starting salary for 2004

£16,000
Scotland

£20,000
Regions

£28,000
London

Universities that DLA plan to visit in 2003-4

Birmingham, Bristol, Cardiff, Dundee, Durham, Exeter, Leeds, Leicester, Liverpool, Manchester, Newcastle, Nottingham, Sheffield, Southampton, Strathclyde, Warwick

Please check with your university careers service for details of events.

Application deadline

31st July 2004

For training contracts commencing in 2006

Contact Details

✉ recruitment.graduate@dla.com

☎ 020 7796 6677

Turn to Page 160 now to request more information about DLA.

DLA is one of the UK's largest commercial law firms with offices in Birmingham, Edinburgh, Glasgow, Leeds, Liverpool, London, Manchester and Sheffield, as well as Antwerp, Brussels, Madrid, Singapore and Shanghai. Last year's fee income totalled £234 million.

Internationally, DLA is part of a cross-border alliance – DLA Group. This operates in 33 major cities across Europe and Asia, allowing DLA to offer a consistent service to clients worldwide. DLA's current vision is to be a top five European full service law firm with a significant presence in Asia.

The firm's clients include some of the world's leading businesses, governments, banks and financial institutions, and their emphasis on providing high quality service and team work results in a challenging and fast-paced working environment.

DLA was ranked 16th in the Sunday Times' '100 Best Companies to Work for' survey in 2003, and was also listed as one of the Financial Times' 'Best Workplaces in the UK and EU' 2003. The firm was named as 'Law Firm of the Year' at the Lawyer awards in 2002, and has achieved the 'Investors in People' accreditation.

DLA look for highly motivated and energetic team players with sound commercial awareness and outstanding communication and organisational skills. Applications are welcomed from students with a minimum of three B's at 'A' level and a 2.1 degree classification (or expected). A formal paid summer vacation scheme runs between June and August each year throughout the UK offices.

Graduate to a better law firm

If you're serious about becoming a commercial lawyer, why not apply to us?

DLA is one of the largest law firms in the world - and we're still growing! Our impressive client base, combined with the emphasis on high quality service and teamwork, provide a challenging fast paced working environment.

We have offices in Birmingham, Edinburgh, Glasgow, Leeds, Liverpool, London, Manchester, Sheffield as well as Antwerp, Brussels, Shanghai and Singapore. We also have associated offices throughout Europe and Asia.

...So why not talk to a firm that's going places?

To find out more about our summer vacation placement scheme, or our training contracts, please contact Sally Carthy, National Graduate Recruitment Manager on 020 796 6677 or visit our website: www.dla.com/recruitment

[dstl]

www.dstl.gov.uk/careers

Vacancies for around 100 graduates in 2004

■ Research & Development

Starting salary for 2004
£Competitive

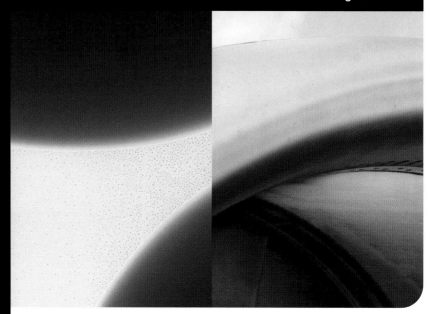

Universities that Dstl plans to visit in 2003-4

Bath, Birmingham, Bristol, Cambridge, Durham, Edinburgh, Exeter, Lancaster, Leeds, London, Loughborough, Manchester, Nottingham, Oxford, Sheffield, Southampton, St Andrews, Strathclyde, Surrey

Please check with your university careers service for details of events.

Application deadline

Rolling Recruitment

Applying early is strongly recommended.

Contact Details

✉ graduates@dstl.gov.uk

☎ 01980 614596
(24 hour answerphone)

Turn to Page 160 now to request more information about Dstl.

Dstl, the Defence Science and Technology Laboratory, is the prime provider of advice and expertise to the Ministry of Defence and wider government on defence-related science and technology issues.

Its work spans the spectrum of science itself, yet much of what the organisation does remains out of the public gaze. This is because its main focus is to protect our national security and the safety of the UK's Armed Forces wherever these are threatened.

Graduates have the chance to be part of an evolving, high-tech organisation that is respected worldwide, working in world-class facilities alongside some of the finest minds in their fields. At Dstl, individuality thrives – people are encouraged to push back the boundaries of conventional thinking.

Enthusiastic and analytically minded graduates are being recruited to follow careers as technical specialists or project managers. They will have a degree in applied sciences, physical sciences, engineering, biological & health sciences, maths, operational analysis or human sciences, along with the flexibility to work either independently or within a team.

Dstl builds on graduates' knowledge with a structured development programme, a Chartership Scheme to help gain membership of an appropriate professional body, a mix of courses, workshops and events, and a 'buddy' to offer advice and guidance. Starting salaries are designed to attract high achievers, while comprehensive benefits include a choice of final salary or stakeholder pension schemes and generous holiday entitlement. Advancement throughout Dstl – and the financial rewards this will bring – is purely on merit.

We can give you this much now... ■ ■■ graduates
■■■ ■■ ■■■ ■■■ ■■■ science ■■■ engineering
■■■ ■■ ■■■ ■■■ ■■■ defence-
■■■ solutions ■■■ ■■ blue sky ■■■ ■
R&D. ■■ original ■■ ■■■ thinking ■■ ■■
national interest ■■ ■ ■■ ■■■ ■ state-of-
the-art ■■■ ■■ ■■ ■■ ■ global
■■■ ■ ■ ■■ ■ expertise... and fill in
the gaps when you work here.

INVESTOR IN PEOPLE

[dstl]

Dstl is part of the Ministry of Defence

At Dstl, innovative scientific thinking delivers solutions that make the world a better place. Our R&D remit is uniquely broad. Our work is highly confidential. Our graduates are constantly stretched in the pursuit of technical excellence, yet they enjoy a healthy work/life balance. All positions are permanent and come with a comprehensive range of benefits, including generous pension and holidays. But to see the full picture, you'll have to join us. So if you are a final year student, recent graduate, graduate with experience or postgraduate, and you have an enquiring mind and an interest in pure research, find out more. See the careers page of our website where you can apply online or, for a brochure and application form, email: graduates@dstl.gov.uk telephone: 01980 614596 (24hr answer phone) or write to: Dstl Graduate Recruitment, Room 17, Building 106, Porton Down, Salisbury, Wiltshire SP4 0JQ. Please quote reference Dstl/TIM09.

www.dstl.gov.uk

\ APPLIED SCIENCES \ PHYSICAL SCIENCES
\ ENGINEERING \ BIOLOGICAL & HEALTH SCIENCES
\ MATHS \ OPERATIONAL ANALYSIS \ HUMAN SCIENCES

☰ ERNST & YOUNG

www.ey.com/uk/graduate

Vacancies for around
250 **graduates in 2004**

- Accountancy
- Finance
- IT

Starting salary for 2004
£Competitive

Universities Ernst & Young plans to visit in 2003-4
Ernst & Young will be visiting a range of universities. Please check their website for full details of events.

Application deadline
Rolling Recruitment
Applying early is strongly recommended.

Contact Details
☎ 0800 289 208
Turn to Page 160 now to request more information about Ernst & Young.

Right for each other?

Ernst & Young helps businesses and organisations to improve their effectiveness and achieve their objectives. It does this by providing clients with a range of expert services – from auditing to tax, from corporate finance to entrepreneurial business development, from economic analysis to IT advice.

The firm's clients include many of the world's most successful companies, together with government, entrepreneurs, small businesses, charities and other organisations throughout the UK.

Ernst & Young is looking for business leaders who can help its clients thrive. It doesn't want 'types'; it wants people with their own unique set of qualities and skills, including individuality, commercial drive, energy, commitment and the ability to work brilliantly in a team.

They offer a graduate programme for those who have what it takes to thrive. The programme is based on real experience, with graduates working on live client projects from day one. Graduates are also given a range of support and career development opportunities, including formal training, career counselling, coaching, mentoring and knowledge management resources. Also, the firm has recently introduced the Accelerated Development Programme – a limited-entry programme enabling its highest performing employees to rapidly develop advanced strategic, people and management skills.

The firm receives many applications, but offers just 250 graduate positions and 150 undergraduate positions each year. Its selection process is rigorous, with priority given to candidates who have the right balance of skills and personality, and who show a clear interest in its business.

Perhaps.

It's impossible to answer that question until you (and we) know more.

You're looking for a place where you can challenge yourself, learn and get the support you need to develop a brilliant career. We're looking for people with the individuality, team-working skills, commercial drive, energy and commitment needed to provide our clients with world-class services.

Interested? Find out more by visiting our website.

www.ey.com/uk/graduate

EVERSHEDS

www.eversheds.com

Vacancies for 92
graduates in 2004

 Law

Starting salary in 2003
£17,000-£28,000
2004 salaries not yet confirmed

**Universities Eversheds
plan to visit in 2003-4**
Aberdeen, Aberystwyth,
Belfast, Birmingham, Bristol,
Cambridge, Cardiff, City,
Dublin, Dundee, Durham,
East Anglia, Edinburgh,
Exeter, Glasgow, Hull,
Lancaster, Leeds, Leicester,
Liverpool, London,
Manchester, Newcastle,
Northumbria, Nottingham,
Nottingham Trent, Oxford,
Reading, Sheffield,
Southampton, St Andrews,
UMIST, Warwick, York
Please check with your university
careers service for details of events.

Application deadline
31st January 2004
for 2004 Vacation Placement Scheme
31st July 2004
for 2006 Training Contract

Contact Details
✉ gradrec@eversheds.com
☎ 0500 994 500
Turn to Page 160 now to request
more information about Eversheds.

**Eversheds is about people. For the facts and figures, check out
the website – but to find out what exactly makes the firm tick,
read on!**

Recognised as one of the world's leading law firms, Eversheds is a success
story, with an innovative approach to the way it does business. Trainees are
the future of the firm. Each person counts, as an individual, because clients do
business with people they respect and like. Being a successful commercial
lawyer is all about an enthusiastic and pragmatic approach to finding the best
commercial solution for one's client.

Eversheds looks for individuals who have three qualities: intellectual ability – a
flexible and enquiring mind; the potential, with training, to develop a real
commercial awareness; and most important of all, a positive image. Clients are
looking for winners, people they can trust and rely on to give them real
solutions to complex business needs.

Right from the outset, the firm invests in its graduates. A blend of on-the-job
training, specialist courses and secondments to clients and other offices is
designed to suit each individual, thus developing knowledge, practical skills
and confidence. Real leadership, giving direction, support and encouragement
is always on hand.

Trainees are expected to use their initiative and, under proper supervision, are
given as much responsibility as they can take. There is a great emphasis on
client contact throughout their training and career.

Eversheds has a genuinely friendly culture. The environment is professional,
supportive and fun!

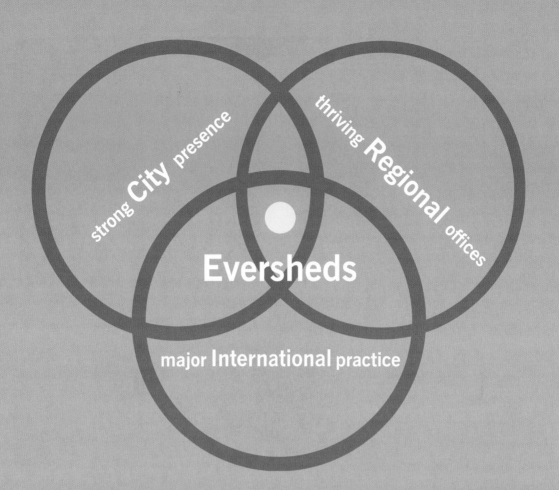

strong **City** presence

thriving **Regional** offices

Eversheds

major **International** practice

Graduate Opportunities

Recognised as one of the world's leading law firms, Eversheds is a success story with an innovative approach to business.

Trainees are the future of the firm. Each person counts, as an individual, because clients do business with people they respect and like.

We are looking for people who believe they can add value in the commercial world. You provide the enthusiasm and intellect and we'll provide a professional, supportive and friendly environment, together with first rate training, to develop you into a really effective business adviser.

For further information, or to apply for a vacation placement or training contract, please visit our website.

 EVERSHEDS

www.eversheds.com

ExxonMobil

www.exxonmobil.com/ukrecruitment

Vacancies for around
50 **graduates in 2004**

- Engineering
- Finance
- IT
- Marketing

Starting salary for 2004
£25,000+

Universities ExxonMobil plans to visit in 2003-4
Aberdeen, Aston, Bath, Birmingham, Bristol, Cambridge, Edinburgh, Exeter, Glasgow, Heriot-Watt, Leeds, London, Loughborough, Manchester, Newcastle, Nottingham, Oxford, Strathclyde, Surrey, UMIST
Please check with your university careers service for details of events.

Application deadline
5th March 2004

Contact Details
☎ 0845 330 8878
Turn to Page 160 now to request more information about ExxonMobil.

ExxonMobil is a worldwide leader in the petroleum and petrochemicals business and has a presence in nearly 200 countries and territories.

Exxon Mobil Corporation is the parent company of the Esso, Mobil and ExxonMobil companies that operate in the United Kingdom within a dynamic, strategically important and exciting business, striving towards operational excellence with an expert talented workforce, strong financial resources and cutting edge technology. Customers are both global and local, ranging from major airlines to individuals who visit service stations worldwide. Chemical products are also manufactured for everything from lipstick to antifreeze.

A diverse range of career opportunities is available within both commercial and technical functions where graduates can expect immediate responsibility and accountability. Analytical skills are essential, as is the ability to think, act and adapt in a global environment with sound judgement and tenacity.

The three-year ExxonMobil Graduate Development Programme is run with the London Business School and covers interpersonal skills, business awareness and people management leading to alumni status of the LBS.

Input from supervisors and mentors helps graduates develop an appropriate career path by reviewing skills and training needs. All graduates develop technical and personal skills via internal, external courses and on-the-job training. Graduates are also encouraged to achieve chartered qualifications where appropriate.

Rapid skills growth and career development is standard and graduates can expect a high degree of intellectual challenge and change.

ExxonMobil

GEOSCIENCE	PRODUCTION & DEVELOPMENT	GAS & POWER MARKETING	MANUFACTURING & DISTRIBUTION	FUELS & CHEMICALS SALES & MARKETING	FINANCE	INFORMATION TECHNOLOGY

How far can you see?

Life beyond university holds immense choice and opportunity; ExxonMobil can offer you both. As a worldwide leader in the petroleum and petrochemicals business we have a vast range of careers to exceed your expectations.

If you are a **Finalist** or **recent Graduate**, we are recruiting people from all degree disciplines into our Graduate Scheme. If you are an **Undergraduate**, we have 12 month industrial placements and 8 week summer placements to offer you real business experience and training to enhance your university studies.

If you visualise yourself in a dynamic, strategically important and exciting business, take a look at our website for more information. Alternatively, for a brochure, please call **0845 330 8878**.

We are an equal opportunities employer.

www.exxonmobil.com/ukrecruitment

explore **new**horiz**o**ns

www.gchq.gov.uk/recruitment

**Vacancies for around
250 graduates in 2004**

- Accountancy
- Engineering
- Finance
- General Management
- IT
- Purchasing

Starting salary for 2004
Please visit GCHQ's website for
salary information.

**Universities that GCHQ
plans to visit in 2003-4**
Please check with your university
careers service for details of events.

Application deadline
Please visit GCHQ's website for
deadline information.

Contact Details

✉ recruitment@
gchq.gsi.gov.uk

Turn to Page 160 now to request
more information about GCHQ.

Government Communications Headquarters (GCHQ) plays a vital role in protecting British interests on the international stage and helps shape the stories that make tomorrow's headlines.

They use some of the world's most sophisticated technology to intercept and interpret telecommunications and electronic signals from around the globe. This information is used to combat international terrorism, keep track of weapons of mass destruction, provide vital military and political intelligence and help detect and prevent serious fraud and crime. In addition, the specialist Communications Electronics Security Group (CESG) advises government and British industry on communications and computer security, and develops systems to ensure that communications networks are 100 per cent secure.

GCHQ invests in the best graduates from a range of disciplines: as well as IT, electronics and engineering specialists, they recruit mathematicians, linguists, librarians, financial and information specialists. All play a key role in keeping GCHQ at the forefront of technology in the fields of computer hardware and software development, satellite and state-of-the-art communications and intelligence techniques. There are also opportunities for non-specialist graduates in intelligence analyst, corporate support and fast-track management careers.

They offer individually tailored training, external and internal development opportunities (such as mentoring, secondments and shadowing), and the chance of sponsorship for professional qualifications.

Please see www.gchq.gov.uk/recruitment for details.

Shock, horror! It's official! Our graduates use intelligence all the time. That's because every day, we gather and collect information, data and electronic signals which are analysed minutely and turned into vital intelligence. This is then used by government and enforcement agencies to form policy and actions which shape the sort of world events you hear about in the news. Our whole business is about intelligence, and you'll need to use yours.

As well as IT, Electronics and Telecommunications specialists, we recruit Mathematicians, Intelligence Analysts, Linguists, Librarians, Information Specialists and Fast Track Management Trainees. Your career will benefit from a culture of continuous personal and professional development designed to make the best of your abilities and keep your knowledge up-to-date. Other personal/lifestyle benefits include flexible hours, well-resourced sports, social and welfare provision and an excellent pension scheme. The location is first class too, based in our new state-of-the-art headquarters in vibrant Cheltenham, which is within easy reach of the Cotswolds, Oxford, Bristol, Birmingham and London.

Our recruitment campaigns start in October and continue throughout the year. Closing dates vary, so please check our website regularly (you can apply on-line) or contact us for more details.

So use your intelligence:

Visit www.gchq.gov.uk/recruitment
Email recruitment@gchq.gsi.gov.uk
Telephone 01242 232912/3 or fax 01242 260108.

To register for a brochure visit www.wherecareersmakeheadlines.co.uk

GCHQ values diversity and welcomes applicants from all sections of the community. We want our workforce to reflect the diversity of our work. Applicants must be British citizens.

GRADUATES
CHELTENHAM

WHERE CAREERS MAKE HEADLINES

INVESTOR IN PEOPLE

GlaxoSmithKline

www.gsk.com/careers

Vacancies for around
50-60 graduates in 2004

- Engineering
- Finance
- Human Resources
- IT
- Logistics
- Marketing
- Purchasing
- Research & Development
- Sales

Starting salary for 2004
£Competitive

Universities that GSK plans to visit in 2003-4
Please check with your university careers service for details of events.

Application deadline
Please check University Relations pages on website for further details.

Contact Details
Turn to Page 160 now to request more information about GSK.

GlaxoSmithKline (GSK) is one of the world's leading research-based pharmaceutical companies. Over 100,000 people worldwide are dedicated to delivering innovative medicines and products that help millions do more, feel better and live longer.

Their pharmaceutical segment generated over £18 billion of sales in prescription medicines and vaccines in 2002, and they are leaders in four major therapeutic areas – anti-infectives, central nervous system, respiratory and gastro-intestinal/metabolic. In the consumer healthcare sector, they are equally successful, with £3.2 billion of sales from a portfolio comprising of over-the-counter medicines, oral care products and nutritional healthcare drinks, many of which are household names as well as market-leading brands.

Bringing these medicines and products to patients requires the combined effort of everyone in the company. Over 42,000 manufacturing staff, for example, turn chemicals into products that can be used easily and effectively, while over 40,000 marketing and sales staff bring those products to patients. In focusing on solving their challenges, their size and opportunities enable them to make a difference to healthcare and society worldwide.

Every second, they distribute more than 35 doses of vaccines. Every minute, more than 1,100 prescriptions are written for their products. Every hour, they spend more than £277,000 to find new medicines. Every day, more than 200 million people around the world use a GSK brand toothbrush or toothpaste.

Their strategic intent is to become the undisputed leader in their industry, a responsibility shared by each and every employee. Graduates at GSK will play an integral part in achieving this goal.

Choose a career for all the right reasons.

Life's full of choices, especially when you're a graduate. Hundreds of organisations know that you've got the intelligence, enthusiasm and vitality they need. And they'll promise you the world in return.

In essence, GlaxoSmithKline is no different – which is why the people who join our graduate development programme enjoy one of the best benefits packages around, including a competitive starting salary, bonus opportunities and 26 days' holiday.

But that's not all. We appreciate that there are some things money just can't buy. So we also offer you the chance to help someone else lead a longer, healthier, happier life. Because we know from our own experience that there's no other feeling like it.

For a full listing of current opportunities, please visit our website at www.gsk.com. All data processed in accordance with the provisions of the Data Protection Act. Developing talent through equality of opportunity.

Together we can make life better.

Goldman Sachs

www.gs.com/careers

Vacancies for around 250-350 **graduates in 2004**

- Finance
- Human Resources
- Investment Banking
- IT

Vacancies also available in Europe

Starting salary for 2004
£Competitive

Universities that Goldman Sachs plans to visit in 2003-4
Please check with your university careers service for details of events.

Application deadline
November 2003
Full time graduate positions
January 2004
Summer internship
Please visit website for further details.

Contact Details
Turn to Page 160 now to request more information about Goldman Sachs.

Goldman Sachs is a leading global investment banking, securities and investment management firm that provides a wide range of services worldwide to a substantial and diversified client base, including corporations, financial institutions, governments and high-net-worth individuals.

The firm operates its businesses on a closely coordinated and integrated global basis, serving its clients through teams of highly qualified professionals. It combines profound knowledge of local markets with international execution capabilities and, as the global economy evolves, it diversifies constantly to help its clients capitalise on opportunities wherever they are in the world.

Goldman Sachs' ability to meet these challenges depends on attracting and retaining the highest quality people from a wide range of university courses and backgrounds. The firm takes an unusual effort to identify the best person for every job and at the same time is committed to providing equal employment opportunities to all qualified persons.

The firm operates through a number of specialised divisions and the career opportunities and challenges differ within these. The recruitment process aims to identify a 'personal' fit between the individual and their chosen division.

Academic discipline and understanding of finance are less important than the personal qualities an individual brings with them. It is intellect, personality and zest for life that is valued the most. Goldman Sachs expects commitment, enthusiasm and drive from its employees but, in return, offers unparalleled exposure, early responsibility, significant rewards and unlimited career opportunities.

INSIDE EVERY TALENTED PERSON IS AN EVEN MORE TALENTED PERSON TRYING TO GET OUT.

You know that there's so much more you want to achieve. And that voice inside that drives you to seek the next challenge is about to be heard. At Goldman Sachs, you'll be surrounded by like-minded teammates who share this passion to succeed. Our training programmes are a vital part of our culture and are a way for you to realise your potential. Your coaching and mentoring start when you start, and they never stop. To be part of it, we encourage you to find out more. Something tells us you've been waiting to make this leap.

WWW.GS.COM/CAREERS

Grant Thornton

Vacancies for around 110 graduates in 2004

■ Accountancy

■ Finance

Starting salary for 2004
£11,000-£20,000

Universities that Grant Thornton plans to visit in 2003-4
Birmingham, Cardiff, East Anglia, Edinburgh, Glasgow, Leeds, London, Loughborough, Newcastle, Nottingham, Sheffield, Southampton, Sussex, Warwick
Please check with your university careers service for details of events.

Application deadline
Rolling Recruitment
Applying early is strongly recommended.

Contact Details
Turn to Page 160 now to request more information about Grant Thornton.

A career with Grant Thornton means having the backing of a truly successful and well established organisation. A leading UK firm of financial and business advisers to entrepreneurial businesses and their owners, Grant Thornton's network of member firms spans over 110 countries, bringing together 22,000 personnel in around 600 offices worldwide.

Grant Thornton offer a first-class training programme in a relaxed environment, providing experience in various aspects of their business activities as well as the technical skills required to pass the professional exams.

Graduate positions are initially offered in audit, tax and recovery and re-organisation, although Grant Thornton's breadth of services mean there are many other career paths to pursue upon qualification, including corporate finance, forensic and investigation and risk management services. Opportunities for development and learning begin right from day one with regular career planning and the chance for early responsibility and promotion.

Grant Thornton are looking for graduates who are motivated and enthusiastic, think intelligently yet practically, and are able to work well in a team. Applicants should have a good academic record and be expecting a 2.2 honours degree or better in any discipline. A minimum of 300 UCAS points or 24 'A' level points is required for ACA, CA and CTA training, and for ACCA a minimum of 240 UCAS points or 20 'A' level points is required. All applicants must have a minimum of grade B in GCSE Mathematics and English Language.

More information and an online application is available on their website at www.grant-thornton.co.uk

Career development with an **Individual Perspective** at Grant Thornton…

…it's not just about passing your exams and gaining your professional qualification, but about **developing the individual in you**. To find out more about an interesting, challenging and rewarding career in an environment where your unique perspective is encouraged, visit us at **www.grant-thornton.co.uk**

Grant Thornton 🕳

Advisers to the independently minded

 **HBOS**plc

www.hbos-futures.co.uk

Vacancies for around
120 graduates in 2004

- Accountancy
- Finance
- General Management
- Human Resources
- IT
- Retailing

Starting salary for 2004
£18,000-£25,000

Universities that HBOS
plans to visit in 2003-4
Please check with your university
careers service for details of events.

Application deadline
See website for further details

Contact Details
Turn to Page 160 now to request
more information about HBOS.

Since the merger of Halifax and Bank of Scotland in 2001, HBOS plc has gone from strength to strength.

One of the largest financial services organisations in Europe with an unrivalled 25 million customers, the market-leading line-up of HBOS brands includes award-winning companies like Esure, Clerical Medical and Intelligent Finance.

As a new force in banking with the means and expertise to challenge the 'Big 4' clearing banks, HBOS can offer customers the value, innovation and choice they deserve and give the brightest graduates everything they need to become the most effective, inspiring managers of the future. So, what can graduates expect? If it's an environment that will support their desire for career progression and personal growth, then that's exactly what they'll find at HBOS.

The exact nature of training depends on which business graduates join, and which specialist career path they choose – every graduate scheme is tailored to the needs of each business area, as well as the individual's professional aspirations. But one thing is consistent whichever division graduates join: HBOS strongly believes in the benefits of providing continuing professional development and opportunity for promotion.

The programmes are designed to fast track graduates to senior positions within the company and offer personal development and technical training specific to their role. This will be a combination of internal and external training and, where appropriate, will lead to a professional qualification.

In the end, however high graduates' expectations, HBOS can meet them, with market-leading training and development for the whole of the scheme – and beyond.

Swati's 27. Twenty five million customers use her IT expertise.

What do you expect?

GRADUATES

£18,000 - £25,000   UK wide

Created by the merger of Halifax and Bank of Scotland, HBOS can provide you with exposure to a mind-opening breadth of career opportunities. For 2004, we are offering about 100 vacancies in areas such as General Management, Corporate Banking, HR, Actuarial, Finance, Estate Agency and IT. Our vacancies are spread throughout the UK with locations from Edinburgh to London and Bristol to Aberdeen with all programmes providing structured training and development. Does this sound like your kind of company? Find out more at **www.hbos-futures.co.uk**

Equal opportunities for all - our policy is as simple as that.

POSITIVE ABOUT DISABLED PEOPLE

BANK OF SCOTLAND   **HALIFAX**

HBOSplc

HSBC ◆X◆

The world's local bank

www.hsbc.com/graduates

Vacancies for around
350 **graduates in 2004**

- Accountancy
- Finance
- General Management
- Investment Banking
- IT

Vacancies also available in Europe,
Asia and elsewhere in the world

Starting salary for 2004
£Competitive

**Universities that HSBC
plan to visit in 2003-4**

Aberystwyth, Aston, Bangor,
Bath, Belfast, Birmingham,
Bristol, Cambridge, Cardiff,
Durham, Edinburgh,
Lancaster, Leeds, Liverpool,
London, Loughborough,
Manchester, Newcastle,
Nottingham, Nottingham
Trent, Oxford, Oxford Brookes,
Reading, Sheffield,
Southampton, St Andrews,
Sussex, UMIST, Warwick
Please check with your university
careers service for details of events.

Application deadline
5th December 2003
Please visit the HSBC website for
further details.

Contact Details
Turn to Page 160 now to request
more information about HSBC.

HSBC is the world's local bank, and the HSBC Group is one of the world's largest financial organisations. They operate in 80 countries and territories worldwide, which is why they're able to offer so many different things to all sorts of different people.

HSBC recruit graduates of any discipline on to all of their programmes. They prepare graduates for management and executive positions in Commercial Banking, Finance, Insurance, International Management, Information Technology, and Corporate, Investment Banking & Markets, Group Private Banking & Asset Management.

The experiences of graduates will be rich and varied whatever part of HSBC's business they join. Among them will be first-class training that develops individuals both personally and professionally. HSBC will help graduates develop a career that suits both their abilities and ambitions.

Graduates will be given early responsibility, sometimes more than they may be expecting, and will have the chance to work with teams from a range of business areas across the Group. HSBC offer chances to work both within the UK and internationally.

For those who can seize opportunities and make a real difference to how HSBC do business, the Group will give them the exposure and practical business experience they need to become a world-class leader locally, nationally or internationally.

Further details on the programmes and how to apply can be found on the graduate website, www.hsbc.com/graduates

▶ adrenalin rush

One of countless experiences now available from HSBC.

Chances are, whatever your role with us, you'll give presentations. And whether they're to a couple of people, or a couple of hundred, you'll be well prepared. Our investment in your training and development is substantial. And it will help you harness every molecule of adrenalin generated by facing fresh experiences daily.

They're experiences that are exceptionally wide-ranging. We offer graduates many different roles within Commercial Banking, Finance, Insurance, International Management, Information Technology and Corporate Investment Banking & Markets,

Group Private Banking & Asset Management. Whatever you're looking for – a generalist management career or the opportunity to specialise; overseas opportunities or a fast-track UK-based career; the chance to motivate people or to influence global markets – you can find it here. Perhaps that's one of the reasons why we're now ranked No.6 in the Times Top 100 Graduate Employers Survey.

For a cross-section of the kind of experiences you can tap into, please visit **www.hsbc.com/graduates** and browse.

HSBC ◆❳❲◆

The world's local bank

Graduate opportunities

Issued by HSBC Bank plc

Vacancies for graduates in 2004 are to be confirmed

- Consulting
- IT
- Research & Development
- Sales

Starting salary in 2003
£21,000-£24,000

Universities that IBM plan to visit in 2003-4

Aston, Bath, Birmingham, Bradford, Bristol, Brunel, Cambridge, City, Durham, Edinburgh, Glasgow, Lancaster, Leeds, London, Loughborough, Manchester, Newcastle, Northumbria, Nottingham, Nottingham Trent, Oxford, Oxford Brookes, Plymouth, Sheffield, Southampton, UMIST, Warwick, York
Please check with your university careers service for details of events.

Application deadline
Rolling Recruitment
Applying early is strongly recommended. See website for further information.

Contact Details

✉ 3grad@uk.ibm.com

☎ 023 9256 4015

Turn to Page 160 now to request more information about IBM.

IBM is the world's largest information technology company. They strive to lead in the creation, development and manufacture of the industry's most advanced information technologies, and translate these advanced technologies into value for IBM customers through their professional solutions, consulting and services worldwide.

IBM have developed technology to distribute digital music and capture images from Mars, and have helped build, run and host websites for the world's most popular sporting events, including Wimbledon and the Ryder Cup.

With more than 300,000 staff in over 100 countries and with its newly acquired business consulting, the career opportunities are vast. In 2003 IBM was voted the second most popular company among graduates looking for their dream job (totaljobs.com) and ranked in the top 20 in the UK's Best Places to Work Survey, conducted by the Financial Times.

To be considered, graduates should have a minimum of 24 UCAS points or equivalent and be expecting or have a 2.1 honours degree or higher. Whilst the degree discipline does not matter, candidates' personal attributes and skills are of key importance. Graduates need to be excellent communicators, keen team players, have a high degree of drive, and be able to demonstrate first class analytical skills and a passion for working in IT.

IBM prides itself on the quality of training offered to its employees. Graduates benefit from a range of educational offerings tailored to their individual needs to ensure that they have the skills necessary to be successful. IBM promotes internal qualifications and often facilitates external professional qualifications.

www.**ibm.com**/employment/uk

REASON #103 to work at IBM

Innovation doesn't have to wear a suit and tie.

www.moreforgraduates.com   www.jaguarcareers.com   www.landrovercareers.com

Vacancies for around 30 **graduates in 2004**

- Engineering
- Finance
- Human Resources
- IT
- Marketing
- Purchasing
- Sales

Starting salary for 2004
£21,000-£23,000

Universities that Jaguar & Land Rover plan to visit in 2003-4
Please check with your university careers service for details of events.

Application deadline
Apply from September
Applying early is strongly recommended.

Contact Details
Turn to Page 160 now to request more information about Jaguar & Land Rover.

Everyone's heard of Jaguar and Land Rover – two icons of the global automotive industry. But behind these famous brands lies a less well-known fact: increasingly, Jaguar and Land Rover are operating not as separate businesses but as a single company.

Sharing resources, purchasing power and expertise, both organisations are seeing real business benefits from this approach – and so too will the ambitious graduates who join the company in their 2004 intake, who can look forward to more variety, more learning and more chances to progress in the future. More than that, they will each be making their own individual contribution, not just to today's top sellers like the award-winning Range Rover and Jaguar's brand new, all-aluminium XJ saloon – but also to the exciting new vehicles of tomorrow.

Principal operations are centred in Coventry, Birmingham, Solihull, Warwickshire and Merseyside so graduates must be flexible to work in any of these locations. But wherever graduates are based they find that this is a company that's committed to learning and development throughout the graduate scheme, and their whole career.

Graduates will benefit from a highly tailored training programme and the guidance and support of Personal Development Committees – all designed to maximise their professional development. Add to that the fact that graduates will be actively encouraged to study for further qualifications, such as chartered status or an MBA, and it all combines to make a compelling package.

Not so long ago graduates were faced with a tough choice – Jaguar? Or Land Rover? Today, you can have the best of both.

Performance²

Chances are you want to work with a well-known, powerful, inspirational brand. A brand that can offer you great development opportunities and the scope to achieve more. Well, what if you could work with two such brands? Jaguar and Land Rover are demonstrating the benefits of working together as a unified force in an incredibly competitive marketplace: sharing knowledge and achieving success through technical excellence and a fresher, 'leaner' approach to everything they do. It's double the challenge, double the opportunity and it won't be an easy ride. We are recruiting for the following functions:

Product Development, Manufacturing Operations, Systems/IT, Marketing, Sales and Service, Finance, Purchasing and Human Resources.

To find out more and to apply online, please visit our websites:
www.moreforgraduates.com   www.jaguarcareers.com   www.landrovercareers.com

www.kpmg.co.uk/brightminds

Vacancies for around
500 graduates in 2004

■ **Accountancy**

■ **Finance**

Starting salary for 2004
£Highly Competitive

Universities that KPMG
plan to visit in 2003-4

Bath, Birmingham, Bristol,
Cambridge, Cardiff,
Durham, Edinburgh, Exeter,
Glasgow, Leeds, London,
Manchester, Newcastle,
Nottingham, Oxford, Sheffield,
Warwick, York
Please check with your university
careers service for details of events.

Application deadline
Rolling Recruitment
Early application is recommended.

Contact Details

☎ **0500 664 665**

Turn to Page 160 now to request
more information about KPMG.

All bright minds welcome

One of the leading firms of business advisers, KPMG focuses on finding the right answers for its clients by using teamwork and diversity of thought.

KPMG's global network has offices in 150 countries, providing financial advisory, assurance and tax services. Currently they are recruiting graduates for their 23 UK offices and each could provide a career at the heart of business decision making.

The early years at KPMG are all about learning the job and passing the exams crucial to a future career. The training is tough, but KPMG provides a supportive learning and development network to help individuals realise their potential.

Graduates choose KPMG because they like the culture, honesty, sense of community and the people, who share a passion for delivering the very best service for their clients. KPMG also believes in rewarding their people, offering a competitive salary, pension scheme, life insurance, lunch allowance and interest-free loans of up to £7,000 for graduates.

There are 13 career routes open to graduates. These include Assurance, Tax, Corporate Recovery, Corporate Finance, Information Risk Management, Public Sector Assurance, Pensions & Actuarial consulting, and Regulatory Services. The Business Foundation Programme, the KPMG Management Training Programme and the Public Sector Business Advisor Programme are designed for those who want broad business training or an MBA.

KPMG welcome bright graduates from all disciplines. To find out more and apply online, visit www.kpmg.co.uk/brightminds

TAP

TAP

TAP

TAP TAP

Life would be dull if we all thought the same.

www.kpmg.co.uk/brightminds

To one person, it's a water source. To another, it's a beer pump. To someone else, it's a listening device. A cross-pollination of ideas can lead to better solutions to a problem.

It's this sense of diversity and teamwork that we foster at KPMG where we look for different ways to find the right answer to business problems.

Now we are looking for bright graduates to join one of the leading firms of business advisers. We can offer you 13 different entry routes, 23 offices across the UK and opportunities to gain

a professional qualification or an MBA. A career at KPMG could put you at the heart of business decision making.

You could be part of a team advising the Government on the housing crisis. Or arranging a company flotation. Or even restructuring a business to save jobs. Naturally you won't be leading a team from day one but we'll begin to train you in all-round business skills straight away.

To find out how you can put your mind to work at KPMG go online and tap (oh look, there's another one) in our web address.

You don't need a business or economics degree – If you have at least 24 UCAS points (300 UCAS Tariff points) and are on course for a 2:1, apply online at www.kpmg.co.uk/brightminds and we'll get back to you within one working day.

All bright minds welcome

L'ORÉAL

www.loreal.co.uk

Vacancies for around 30-40 graduates in 2004

- Engineering
- Finance
- General Management
- Logistics
- Marketing
- Sales

Starting salary for 2004
£Competitive

Universities L'Oréal plans to visit in 2003-4
Bristol, Cambridge, Cardiff, Edinburgh, London, Manchester, Nottingham, Oxford, Swansea, UMIST, Warwick
Please check with your university careers service for details of events.

Application deadline
31st December 2003

Contact Details
✉ recruitment@uk.loreal.com
☎ 0800 028 2364
Turn to Page 160 now to request more information about L'Oréal.

COFFEE BAR, L'ORÉAL HAMMERSMITH

Number one worldwide in cosmetics, L'Oréal is the name behind international brands that include L'Oréal Paris, Garnier, Maybelline, Ralph Lauren fragrances and Giorgio Armani fragrances.

Employing some 50,000 people in 130 countries, their cutting edge research and rapid international development have contributed to 18 years of consecutive double-digit growth and sales of over 14.2 billion euros.

Each year L'Oréal takes on around 25 of the most talented graduates from a wide range of university courses, nationalities and backgrounds. There are no specific requirements in terms of degree subject or languages.

Graduates join as Management Trainees and immediately enter into an individually tailored training programme. The programme is modular and provides the opportunity to experience different areas of activity within the business. Management Trainees are expected to make a tangible contribution to the business while increasing their skills and knowledge. Once training is complete, usually after 12 months, graduates start work in their chosen field. How far and fast they progress is based on talent and performance – currently over 460 managers of 50 nationalities work outside their country of origin.

L'Oréal also offers a range of internship opportunities and runs two worldwide competitions for students. The L'Oréal Marketing Award offers student teams the chance to develop their creativity by competing to create a new brand. The E-Strat challenge is played online and gives students the opportunity to practise strategic management. Taking part in either game, or having an internship with the company, is the ideal introduction to a career with L'Oréal.

Linklaters

Vacancies for around
125 graduates in 2004

■ Law

Vacancies also available in Asia

Starting salary for 2004
£28,500

Universities Linklaters
plans to visit in 2003-4
Birmingham, Bristol,
Cambridge, Cardiff, Dublin,
Durham, Exeter, Leeds,
Leicester, London,
Manchester, Nottingham,
Oxford, Sheffield,
Southampton, Warwick
Please check with your university
careers service for details of events.

Application deadline
Please see Linklaters' website for
deadline details.

Contact Details

✉ graduate.recruitment@linklaters.com

☎ 020 7456 2000

Turn to Page 160 now to request more
information about Linklaters.

Linklaters is a global law firm that advises the world's leading
companies, financial institutions and governments. With offices
in major business centres in Europe, Asia and the Americas, the
firm specialises in delivering innovative solutions for its clients'
most challenging deals and assignments.

Linklaters' business covers three core areas – corporate, finance & projects,
and commercial – and over 20 different practices in which trainees can gain
experience. These include M&A, capital markets, banking, projects, asset
finance, real estate, litigation, intellectual property, IT & communications,
EU/competition, employment and tax.

Linklaters is the place for creative problem solvers who enjoy a challenge and
strive for excellence in everything they do. Graduates will learn from colleagues
at the peak of their profession and benefit from being part of a firm with solid
coaching. The firm's open-door policy ensures that graduates always have
access to a mentor, because Linklaters prides itself on strong teamwork, both
within the firm and with its clients.

Before starting the LPC, graduates will complete a unique Business
Foundation Course, which gives a fascinating insight into the firm's and its
clients' business. Linklaters keeps in touch with trainees at Law School through
its LPC Liaison Programme, and when they start work will agree a seat plan of
four six-month seats, tailored to the individual's specific strengths and
interests. Almost all Linklaters trainees spend time in one of the firm's
international offices or on client secondment, and will also receive one of the
best graduate remuneration packages in London.

Big deals, not package deals.
Linklaters

Not all global law firms are the same. At Linklaters we specialise in the most challenging deals and the toughest transactions. Operating as an integrated team of creative problem solvers, we deliver innovative solutions to clients worldwide.

Our vacation scheme offers you the chance to gain first-hand experience of the most complex and exciting assignments in the practice area(s) of your choice. You will also participate in a lecture programme, team exercises and individual project work. If you apply for our Summer Exchange Programme you may be able to spend a couple of weeks in one of our other European offices. And you'll find that life at Linklaters isn't all work and no play. Thanks to our evening events, you'll enjoy an active social life too.

If you want to find out more about what it takes to succeed in one of the world's largest and most dynamic law firms, why not apply?

For our Christmas scheme, contact us by 21 November 2003. For our summer schemes, your application must be in by 31 January 2004.

Contact
Telephone: (44-20) 7456 2000
Email: graduate.recruitment@linklaters.com
www.linklaters.com/careers/uk

Lloyds TSB

Vacancies for around
80-100 graduates in 2004

- Accountancy
- Finance
- General Management

Vacancies also available in Europe
and elsewhere in the world

Starting salary for 2004
£21,000-£27,000

**Universities Lloyds TSB
plans to visit in 2003-4**

Bath, Birmingham, Bristol,
Cambridge, Cardiff, Durham,
Edinburgh, Exeter, Leeds,
London, Loughborough,
Manchester, Nottingham,
Oxford, Sheffield,
Southampton, Warwick, York
Please check with your university
careers service for details of events.

Application deadline
31st December 2003

Contact Details

✉ graduates@lloydstsb.co.uk
Turn to Page 160 now to request
more information about Lloyds TSB.

The Lloyds TSB Group is one of the UK's leading financial organisations. Offering a huge diversity of personal and corporate finance services, the Lloyds TSB, Scottish Widows and C&G brands are recognised and relied upon by millions.

So their business reaches much farther than the High Street – employing over 80,000 people across 29 countries worldwide. And the opportunities for graduates are just as diverse. Lloyds TSB recognises the importance of talented people to the future of their business. They look for graduates with the ambition, drive and potential to lead the business as a whole – not just with one set of skills for one particular role.

Graduates can join the Group on one of four broad leadership programmes: Wholesale & International Banking, UK Retail Banking, Insurance & Investments, or IT & Operations. They also offer a professional programme in Finance, linked to the CIMA qualification. Whichever programme graduates choose, their training will be tailored to accelerate their individual potential.

Developing people has always been critical to the Lloyds TSB business. They even have their own award-winning corporate university. They work to develop leadership potential in a dynamic, challenging environment – combining formal business-related courses with a series of placements to help graduates become a fully-qualified professional. And they expect graduates to take control of their own career and development.

Lloyds TSB are looking for people who make things happen. High academic achievers, with energy, initiative and exceptional interpersonal, problem-solving and teamwork skills. To find out more, visit www.lloydstsbgraduate.co.uk

Must be the favourite.

Money isn't everything. But that's easy for us to say. We're a bank. The simple truth is, it's difficult making the transition from student to professional. And a starting salary of £27,000* certainly helps.

Obviously, paying well doesn't make us a good employer. But it does show that when we pick someone for our leadership programmes, we're making a serious, long-term commitment to their career.

So whether you're helping us to develop personal banking by mobile phone, taking CIMA qualifications, learning all about corporate banking or finding your feet in insurance, we'll invest the time, money and support needed to help you become one of our top people.

And because money really isn't everything, we'll also offer you an outstanding work/life balance. Get a favourite to back you, visit **www.lloydstsbgraduate.co.uk**

*Starting salary for our 2003 Management Training Programme was £27,450 with London weighting and £24,000 outside London. Due to the cost of supporting them towards CIMA qualification, graduates joining our finance scheme received £24,450 in London and £21,000 outside London.

MARKS & SPENCER

Vacancies for approx.
200 graduates in 2004

 Retailing

Starting salary for 2004
£20,000
Plus benefits and London
weighting as appropriate

Universities that M&S
plan to visit in 2003-4
Please visit the M&S website and
check with your university careers
service for details of events.

Application deadline
12th December 2003

Contact Details
Turn to Page 160 now to request
more information about M&S.

Marks & Spencer is a leading name on the high street. They continue to evolve, bringing together the best talent in the industry. At M&S, people share a unique passion for innovative retailing and outstanding customer service.

The largest clothing retailer in the UK, plans for future growth across key areas of the business including Food, Home and Financial Services are well underway. Marks & Spencer is ranked in the top 20 of this year's Times Top 100 Graduate Employers, and continues to rise each year.

Developing talented people is a high priority and, combined with a determination to dominate every category, has led to a range of exciting new products, practices and profit levels. The dedicated management team lead the way in each new initiative and welcomes graduates with a passion for new ideas, teamwork and meeting challenges head on.

The roles offered to graduates are primarily in Store Management, with some opportunities also available in Head Office. Evidence of personal drive, common sense and focus is essential. Interviews and assessment events offer candidates the chance to demonstrate their passion for retail along with other key skills such as the ability to manage and engage effectively with a range of people.

The company offers a unique training ground for developing retail expertise and management skills. All graduates undertake a formal induction and a structured training programme. Within 12 months of on-the-job training, most graduates are primed for their first management role. For more information, please visit www.marksandspencer.com/passionforretail

Passion for retail?

MARKS & SPENCER

find out more
www.marksandspencer.com

tickled pink

Marks and Spencer p.l.c. is an equal opportunities employer.

POSITIVE ABOUT DISABLED PEOPLE

BEST WORKPLACES UK 2003

Masterfoods

www.mars.com/university

Vacancies for around
25-35 **graduates in 2004**

- Engineering
- Finance
- IT
- Marketing
- Research & Development
- Sales

Vacancies also available in Europe

Starting salary for 2004
£25,000

**Universities Masterfoods
plan to visit in 2003-4**
Please visit the events & activities
page on the website.

Application deadline
12th November 2003

Contact Details
✉ mars.graduate@
eu.effem.com
☎ 01753 514999

Turn to Page 160 now to request
more information on Masterfoods.

Mars Incorporated is a world leader in each of its main businesses – branded snack foods, petcare products, main-meal foods, automated payment systems and drinks vending. With over 170 sites in more than 60 countries worldwide, Mars employs some 30,000 associates and has an annual turnover in excess of $14 billion.

In the UK, Masterfoods forms the largest part of Mars and is responsible for their branded petcare, snackfood and main-meal food businesses.

Working for Masterfoods is different. It is still privately owned and has total freedom to run and develop its business. Masterfoods has a dynamic culture, focussed on making work a stimulating and satisfying place to be. The business has an unusually small number of associates, which means managers and trainees enjoy challenging work and a high degree of accountability. Graduates who join have real freedom to make a difference – doing real jobs, with real responsibility, from day one.

This year, Masterfoods is extending the range of graduate development programmes that they offer, all of which fast track to an exciting and rewarding career. Masterfoods believes there is strength in diversity and welcomes graduates from a variety of ethnic backgrounds and cultures. Masterfoods is international in its approach to doing business and a significant proportion of trainees are recruited from across Europe. There are many opportunities to work or travel overseas.

Masterfoods' approach to graduate development offers stimulating and diverse opportunities to those with the ability to make the most of them.

www.mcdonalds.co.uk

Vacancies for around
70 graduates in 2004

General Management

Retailing

Starting salary for 2004
£17,000-£20,000
Dependent on location

Universities McDonald's
plans to visit in 2003-4
Please check with your university
careers service for details of events.

Application deadline
Rolling Recruitment
Applying early is strongly
recommended.

Contact Details

managementrecruitment@uk.mcd.com

☎ 020 8700 7007

Turn to Page 160 now to request more
information about McDonald's.

With over 1,200 restaurants in the UK, McDonald's are part of everyday life for many people. Yet there is a lot more to the business than might at first be imagined – because McDonald's today is made up of thousands of personal success stories.

Many of the restaurants have a £million plus turnover and employ a team of 60 or more people, which makes running one of them commercial management in its fullest sense. Restaurant Managers take control of every aspect of their restaurant – they set targets, plan budgets, control stock, recruit and train their team, create marketing campaigns and build bridges with the local community.

With the real possibility of making Restaurant Manager within two or three years, there are no limits on where graduates end up or how fast they'll get there. There is, however, a common starting point: Trainee Business Manager. This is the beginning of an intensive 19-week training programme that gives a thorough grounding in the business and builds a whole raft of commercial skills. Step by step, the talents needed for a long-term management career are developed, with trainees proving themselves at every stage as they progress through 2nd and 1st Assistant Manager to Restaurant Manager and beyond.

Degree discipline isn't important – but the ability to get the best out of a team and set the tone of a restaurant is something needed in abundance. Above and beyond that is the need to balance a decisive attitude with a sensitive approach. Good managers are the engines behind the restaurants, so they need to combine energy and ideas with flexibility, commitment and an appetite for hard work. Add a talent for getting the most out of the day by delegating and organising themselves and others, and they should be a great success.

The first couple of weeks were tricky.
There was I, smarty pants History graduate,
in charge of people who'd done the job for years.
Trust was a bit thin on the ground at first.
Then we had our first night out. Amazing what
a bit of Elvis on the karaoke can do. We were
all up there, belting out "We can't go on
together with suspicious minds". Bit apt
when you think about it.

Trainee Business Managers   £17,000-£20,000*

Getting results through other people. In some businesses that's just a piece of
HR speak, but join us as a Trainee Business Manager and you'll find it has real
meaning. We'll turn your gift for getting on with people into invaluable people
management skills. Then we'll add marketing, finance and operations training
into the mix, making you a fully-rounded manager. In next to no time, you'll be
running your own £multi-million business: a McDonald's restaurant. To write
your own story, please go to the careers section of our website, where you can
apply online. Or see our profile opposite for more details.

www.mcdonalds.co.uk

*dependent on location

INVESTOR IN PEOPLE

Every one tells a story

MERCER
Human Resource Consulting

www.mercergrads.co.uk

Vacancies for around
90 **graduates in 2004**

- Consulting
- Finance

Starting salary in 2003
£21,000-£24,000

Universities that Mercer plans to visit in 2003-4
Aston, Bath, Belfast, Birmingham, Bristol, Cambridge, City, Durham, Edinburgh, Exeter, Glasgow, Heriot-Watt, Leeds, Liverpool, London, Manchester, Newcastle, Nottingham, Oxford, Sheffield, Southampton, Strathclyde, UMIST, Warwick, York
Please check with your university careers service for details of events.

Application deadline
Rolling Recruitment
Applying early is strongly recommended.

Contact Details
✉ graduates@mercer.com
☎ 020 7963 3190
Turn to Page 160 now to request more information about Mercer.

Mercer Human Resource Consulting is one of the world's leading consulting organisations, with some 13,000 staff in 40 countries.

Partnering with clients in all aspects of strategic and operational HR consulting, advice is offered in such areas as retirement provision, investment, employee motivation, employee health, executive remuneration, employment law and employee communication. Mercer offers vacancies for actuarial trainees, investment analysts, trainee pension consultants, junior HR and international consultants. Successful candidates must demonstrate ambition, the potential to take responsibility early in their career, personal motivation and the ability to thrive in an atmosphere of achievement, service excellence and teamwork.

Candidates must also have 300 UCAS points and be expecting a minimum 2.1 honours degree in a numerate or semi-numerate discipline. Actuarial trainees must have 'A' level Mathematics at grade B or above (or equivalent).

Shortly after joining, graduates begin the training and development programme. This is a structured combination of hands-on technical training and the development of a range of consulting skills. The overall aim of the programme is to provide a foundation for graduates to build on. Mercer will also provide financial and practical support throughout the professional studies period.

Performance and Development Planning is a key part of training and development for all Mercer employees. Graduates work with their allocated performance and development advisor in setting business and personal development goals in line with Mercer's business plan. This should help individuals to realise their full potential within the company.

MERCER
Human Resource Consulting

www.mercergrads.co.uk

 ## Make the right connections

Mercer is a world leader in human resource consulting, and more besides.

Take a closer look and you'll find a broad range of rewarding graduate careers - everything from actuaries and investment analysts to benefit and legal consultants.

In fact, we are the largest recruiter of graduates for actuarial careers in the UK.

We treat every candidate as an individual, not a number. We invest heavily in personal training and development, with ample study leave and, in some cases, a rotation scheme to give you hands on experience of a broad range of our work for clients.

We look for enthusiastic graduates from a range of disciplines, not just mathematics, (although a mathematical aptitude is important - especially if you want to be an actuary).

To get connected to Mercer explore our website or contact:

The Graduate Team
Mercer Human Resource Consulting
38-40 Trinity Square
London EC3N 4DJ
Tel 020 7977 8825
email graduates@mercer.com

www.mercergrads.co.uk

INVESTOR IN PEOPLE

 Marsh & McLennan Companies

MI5
THE SECURITY SERVICE

www.mi5.gov.uk

Vacancies for up to
60 **graduates in 2004**

RECEPTION

Starting salary for 2004
£21,100

**Universities that MI5
plans to visit in 2003-4**
Please check with your university
careers service for details of events.

Application deadline
Rolling Recruitment
Applying early is strongly
recommended. See website for
deadline details.

Contact Details
☎ 0870 241 6608
Bartlett Scott Edgar
(External Recruitment Agency)

Turn to Page 160 now to request
more information about MI5.

The Security Service (MI5) is the UK's security intelligence
agency; protecting national security through the collection,
analysis and dissemination of secret intelligence.

Graduates are likely to be involved initially in assessing and investigating
threats to national security. Over a career, they must be flexible and involved in
a range of roles. Promotion is competitive and by merit, and the most capable
are likely to advance quickly to responsibility for significant aspects of the
Service's work. Skills and personal qualities are more important than degree
subject or result. Well developed analytical and organisational skills, a flexible
approach and a fine eye for detail are essentials. The Service's work, which is
of a highly sensitive nature, demands integrity and reliability too.

The two-year development programme begins with an initial period of intensive
skills training, plus supported learning in the workplace. In addition there are
progress reviews and further development opportunities (internal courses,
visits to key liaison contacts, training in teamwork and leadership skills). As
well as formal training there will be the opportunity to experience other areas of
the Service, broadening understanding of the Service's core businesses and
developing an appreciation of the requirements placed upon them.

The Service aims to reflect the diversity of modern society at all levels. The
Service operates an equal opportunities policy and is committed to the active
promotion of a working environment that is free from discrimination.

Those who apply must be born or naturalised British citizens with at least one
parent also being a British citizen. Discretion is a serious part of working for
the Service; please avoid telling people about your application.

MI5
THE SECURITY SERVICE

Great assumptions about a career at MI5

As an organisation, we're a lot more diverse than you might imagine - there's no such thing as a typical employee. Instead, we're open, supportive and committed to encouraging individuality - so, far from forcing you into a mould, we'll help you make the very most of yourself.

It's worth protecting www.mi5.gov.uk

Microsoft®

www.microsoft.com/uk/graduates

Vacancies for up to
20 **graduates in 2004**

- Consulting
- IT
- Sales

Starting salary for 2004
£23,500

Universities Microsoft plans to visit in 2003-4
Aston, Brunel, Edinburgh, Glasgow, Lancaster, London, Loughborough, Manchester, Reading, UMIST, Warwick
Please check with your university careers service for details of events.

Application deadline
January 2004

Contact Details
✉ gradrec@microsoft.com
Turn to Page 160 now to request more information about Microsoft.

Microsoft Ltd is a subsidiary of Microsoft Corporation. It currently employs over 1,500 people in the UK, and has its headquarters at Thames Valley Park in Reading.

Microsoft has always been driven by a sense of mission – to empower people and businesses to realise their full potential – through being the visionary technology leader in innovative software.

Personal qualities like talent, intelligence, individuality and personality are important. But even more are a genuine passion for what technology can achieve and individual potential – it's not so much what graduates know now, as what they're capable of doing.

What graduates can count on, is that they'll have their thinking challenged. In the first year, whether on the Technical or Sales & Marketing graduate schemes, they'll go through a comprehensive training programme while they work. It's designed to provide them with a firm grounding in the business, and an awareness of the relationships forged with customers and the skills they'll want to develop. And throughout, a mentor will be on hand to advise and support in whichever direction individuals pursue.

It's no secret that Microsoft work in an incredibly fast-paced industry. Everyone has to be at their best, at all times, just to keep up. Rest assured, graduates are coached to identify their particular strengths and then helped to build on them. That way they get to do what they do best – only better. And don't think that as an IT organisation, Microsoft is only interested in graduates with technical qualifications – there are a number of diverse opportunities for people with different skills and aspirations. Visit their website for more information.

Give me one good reason why I should join.

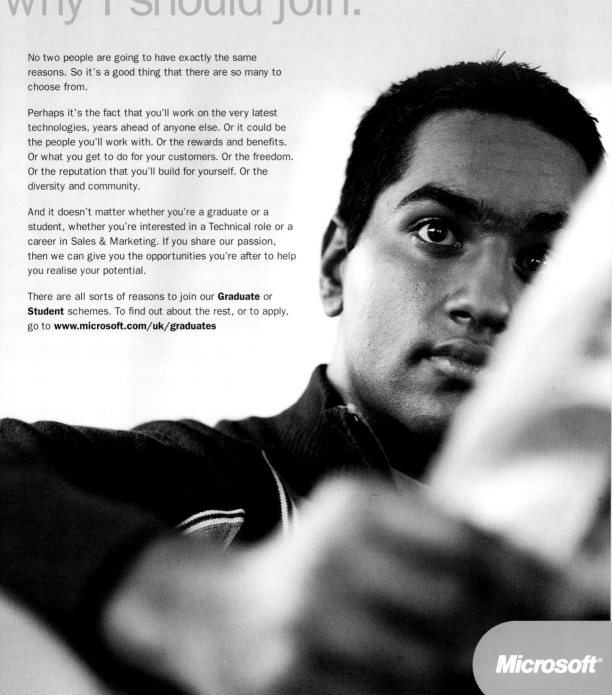

No two people are going to have exactly the same reasons. So it's a good thing that there are so many to choose from.

Perhaps it's the fact that you'll work on the very latest technologies, years ahead of anyone else. Or it could be the people you'll work with. Or the rewards and benefits. Or what you get to do for your customers. Or the freedom. Or the reputation that you'll build for yourself. Or the diversity and community.

And it doesn't matter whether you're a graduate or a student, whether you're interested in a Technical role or a career in Sales & Marketing. If you share our passion, then we can give you the opportunities you're after to help you realise your potential.

There are all sorts of reasons to join our **Graduate** or **Student** schemes. To find out about the rest, or to apply, go to **www.microsoft.com/uk/graduates**

Microsoft®

M°D→RECRUITMENT

www.mod.uk

Vacancies for around 100 **graduates in 2004**

- Accountancy
- Engineering
- Finance
- General Management
- Human Resources
- IT
- Logistics

Starting salary for 2004
£16,000-£23,000
Typically graduates would start on £18,500 depending on experience, degree discipline and grade. Refer to website for more details.

Universities that the MOD plans to visit in 2003-4
The MOD plans to visit universities throughout the year. See the website for dates and locations.

Application deadline
See website for deadline details

Contact Details
Turn to Page 160 now to request more information about the MOD.

The Ministry of Defence is one of the largest, most progressive organisations in the country. A career with them provides a unique opportunity to work at the heart of UK Government, in an organisation that has international influence from the Gulf and the Caribbean to the Balkans and West Africa.

90,000 MOD Civil Servants are employed to formulate defence policy and advise senior Military officers and Ministers, as well as being involved in the many support activities required for such a large organisation – including logistics, finance, contracts, human resources, project management, and IT.

The scope for graduates to find their vocation and develop personal and professional skills in the Ministry of Defence is unique. The MOD will provide them with high-quality, continuous training throughout their career (often leading to the achievement of a relevant professional qualification). Graduates will also have the flexibility to move into new roles or even switch careers altogether, as the MOD itself evolves to meet new demands and priorities.

During their career, graduates may have the opportunity to undertake a period of secondment with Industry, to work in another Government Department or to move between a range of different MOD postings, both in the UK and abroad.

The MOD offers flexible working patterns, a good maternity package and career break options. It is currently taking active steps to increase its representation of people from ethnic minority backgrounds, from women and from people with disabilities – all of whom are currently under-represented throughout the department.

ALL THE DIRECTION YOU NEED.

Unparalleled opportunities for personal and professional development

Locations throughout the UK and overseas, from Project Management at the forefront of technology to Personnel Management and Training

Lots of scope to move internally

Civilians in the Ministry of Defence provide crucial equipment and support to the British Armed Forces, helping in their goal of strengthening international peace and security.

As British Industry's largest single customer, the MOD spends around £10 billion a year on equipment, support and services; and it's important we spend it well. To do that, we rely on recruiting and retaining the very best people from all parts of society.

Every opportunity to find the right career

Our graduate and other programmes are designed to be flexible, so you can move job and location or change career direction if you want to, whilst retaining your status and similar working conditions. This means you can embark on a new career path or choose to study for professional qualifications, whilst continuing your pension and annual leave allowances.

Choice of career paths

Engineering and Science
Project Management
Commercial Officers/Purchasing
Finance
Linguists, Statistician and Medical Staff
Logisticians
Human Resources
Training and Development
Policy
Information Technology

For specific vacancies, see: **www.mod.uk**

MoD→RECRUITMENT

MINISTRY OF DEFENCE

The MOD is an equal opportunity employer aiming for the widest possible diversity in its workforce, drawing recruits from every part of the community. We particularly welcome applications from ethnic minority people, women and people with disabilities who are currently under-represented in the MOD.

Morgan Stanley

www.morganstanley.com/careers

Vacancies for around
160 **graduates in 2004**

- Finance
- Investment Banking
- IT

Starting salary for 2004
£Competitive

**Universities that Morgan
Stanley plans to visit in
2003-4**
Bristol, Cambridge, Dublin,
Edinburgh, London,
Manchester, Oxford,
UMIST, Warwick
Please check with your university
careers service for details of events.

Application deadline
14th November 2003
All graduate applications.
30th January 2004
Summer Internships.

Contact Details
☎ 020 7425 8000 x57575
Turn to Page 160 now to request
more information about Morgan
Stanley.

Morgan Stanley is one of the best-known names in financial
services: a leader in connecting people, ideas and capital to
help its clients achieve their financial aspirations.

The firm has earned a worldwide reputation for the excellence of its advice and
execution in financial markets. Morgan Stanley serves institutional and
individual investors and investment banking clients, including corporations,
governments and other entities around the world.

Truly global, the firm is a market leader in Europe and Asia as well as the
United States: its 54,000 employees work in 600 offices in 27 countries.
Morgan Stanley provides a wide range of services, including underwriting,
trading and research, as well as advice on mergers and acquisitions,
privatisation and financial restructuring. Morgan Stanley also manages $400
billion of investor assets, serves affluent and high net worth individuals in the
United States, Europe and Asia, and provides credit services led by its flagship
Discover Card with more than 50 million U.S. cardmembers.

Morgan Stanley offers graduates a unique combination of global access and
local relevance that make it the most exciting financial services firm in Europe.
Their culture is based on teamwork, a common devotion to excellence, and an
appreciation of personal styles, perspectives and needs. Morgan Stanley
people have the latitude to be themselves and to move up as quickly as they
merit. Whatever a graduate's career aspirations, Morgan Stanley can give them
the tools and the opportunities to achieve them.

Graduate positions are offered within Investment Banking, Fixed Income,
Equity Research, Institutional Equity, IT, and Finance & Operations.

Join Us

morganstanley.com/careers

Experience Leadership

You bring something to your work that no one else does. So does Morgan Stanley. For decades, clients have relied on us consistently for the finest thinking and the most adept execution in financial services.

Morgan Stanley has kept its position as an industry leader year after year by attracting new people to a place where their unique talents can flourish. You can be part of an organisation with the global strength and the market breadth to help clients meet new challenges—and to give you the platform for your own success.

We invite you to move forward with us.

Visit and apply online at:

morganstanley.com/careers/recruiting

Morgan Stanley

Vacancies for around 20 graduates in 2004

- Engineering
- Finance
- Human Resources
- IT
- Logistics
- Marketing
- Purchasing
- Research & Development
- Sales

Starting salary for 2004
c£21,500

Universities that Nestlé plans to visit in 2003-4
Please check with your university careers service for details of events.

Application deadline
Rolling Recruitment
Applying early is strongly recommended.

Contact Details
nestlegrad@uk.nestle.com

Turn to Page 160 now to request more information about Nestlé.

With 230,000 people in 80 countries, 15,000 different products, and a brand portfolio that ranges from Herta, Ski and Kit Kat to Polo and Perrier, Nestlé is the world's largest food company. Yet this is one big business that places the individual at the heart of its culture.

There is also a reluctance to lump people together evident in Nestlé's radical approach to graduate recruitment. Research shows that many graduates are disappointed by their first job. The reality simply doesn't live up to the promise – and perhaps it never could. So is the whole idea of 'management trainees' out of tune with business reality? If an organisation really believes in the potential of the individual, how can they adopt a sheep-dip approach to graduate development?

This is why Nestlé now recruits graduates into real jobs rather than generic 'management training' programmes. Successful applicants are interviewed by line managers and assessed against criteria that are relevant to the job. Training too is tailored to the specific business area. By acknowledging the diversity of the business – and the people who drive it forward – the way is open for steeper learning curves and faster development.

In a performance culture like Nestlé, having a degree doesn't automatically tip a graduate for the top. But having said that, if individuals prove themselves to be an exceptional performer in their early career, they will be considered for accelerated development. This opportunity is not just for graduates, but anyone who has what it takes to be a future leader of the business.

Of course, this is no more than would be expected from a true meritocracy.

A glittering future for people who can swim a mile in their shorts.

In our view, academic qualifications are about as valid a measure of management potential as swimming certificates. Why do you think so many employers drone on about 'being thrown in at the deep end'? The fact is, you can be as intelligent as five dolphins and still have the business sense of a house brick. This is why we don't promise that every graduate we hire will end up on the Board. But we do offer real jobs that matter to us. We also guarantee a chance to prove yourself, not as a trainee, but as a full member of the team. To discover just how far you might go with Nestlé, plunge immediately into **www.nestle.co.uk/recruitment** and click on the 'Young and talented' section.

Nestlé

Good Food, Good Life

Vacancies for around
150 **graduates in 2004**

■ **Finance**
■ **General Management**

Starting salary for 2004
£19,000

Universities that the NHS plan to visit in 2003-4
Aston, Bath, Birmingham, Bradford, Bristol, Brunel, Cambridge, Cardiff, City, Durham, East Anglia, Essex, Exeter, Hull, Keele, Kent, Lancaster, Leeds, Leicester, Liverpool, London, Loughborough, Manchester, Newcastle, Northumbria, Nottingham, Nottingham Trent, Oxford, Oxford Brookes, Plymouth, Reading, Sheffield, Southampton, Surrey, Sussex, UMIST, Warwick, York
Please check with your university careers service for details of events.

Application deadline
5th December 2003

Contact Details
✉ mtsinfo@mts.nhs.uk
☎ 0870 169 9731
Turn to Page 160 now to request more information about the NHS.

The National Health Service provides 24-hour healthcare to the nation, treating one million people every 36 hours. With rising public expectations and tough targets, working for the NHS is one of the most challenging jobs in Britain.

NHS graduate trainees are at the forefront of the current NHS change programme, improving access and services for patients. NHS graduate trainees need to have the strength of character to make tough decisions – they are people who not only cope well with change, but who can lead and shape it.

The NHS needs excellent communicators who will play a key role in determining the NHS of the future, and who reflect the communities they serve.

The NHS offers two graduate training schemes. The Financial Management Scheme offers three years of supported training and study in a programme tailored to the needs and potential of individual trainees. Successful trainees will gain a recognised professional accountancy qualification (CIMA or CIPFA). The General Management Scheme offers a two-year programme of training and development combining early responsibility in placements with a challenging educational programme and the opportunity to work outside of the NHS, in the UK or abroad, for three months. Both schemes provide an orientation, where trainees get to know the NHS inside out, the support of a personal mentor and manager, and a choice of locations across England for their training.

To be eligible for either scheme, applicants must have obtained or be expecting a minimum 2.2 degree in any subject.

Fresh thinkers wanted

This isn't about your first job, it's about your career.

The NHS is Europe's largest employer. It's a £60bn organisation providing 24-hour healthcare to the whole nation, and it's changing fast.

The NHS Plan is an ambitious programme to improve access and services for patients. We need people with talent, drive and commitment to lead this important change. We're looking for tomorrow's leaders, today.

We're recruiting people who are capable of making a difference and who reflect the diversity of the communities we serve. If you think you're ready for a long-term career in one of the most challenging management or finance jobs in Britain, we want to hear from you.

The National Health Service General and Financial Management Training Schemes offer comprehensive training for graduates in England.

Find out more by visiting our website at www.futureleaders.nhs.uk or telephoning 0870 169 9731. Applications for the 2004 intake will be accepted from 1st September to 5th December 2003.

Oxfam

www.oxfam.org.uk/graduate

Vacancies for around 6 graduates in 2004

Marketing

Starting salary for 2004
£15,000

Universities Oxfam plans to visit in 2003-4
Please check with your university careers service for details of events.

Application deadline
March 2004

Contact Details
✉ graduate@oxfam.org.uk
Turn to Page 160 now to request more information about Oxfam.

Wanted: creative, passionate individuals to help change the world.

Oxfam is a development, relief, and campaigning organisation which is working towards a world without poverty.

Oxfam is about people, and people are its greatest resource: 22,000 volunteers help run Oxfam's famous high street shops; over 500,000 individuals make regular donations; more than a million people worldwide support its campaigns; and countless individuals in more than 80 countries work their own way out of poverty, with Oxfam's support.

Oxfam is looking for committed, enthusiastic people to take part in its graduate placement scheme. For those who are passionate about the work and values of Oxfam, and are willing to take on responsibility in this high-profile, professional charity, this could be an ideal opportunity.

Placements are for 14 months and are predominantly in the marketing department, which is responsible for inspiring people to act against poverty – through fundraising, campaigning, and awareness-raising. During the placement, graduates will have the opportunity to work in a number of teams, and gain a wide range of experience in a supportive and stimulating environment. Training will be tailored to the needs of the individual, and mentors will support graduates in their career and personal development.

Oxfam is recruiting graduates to start in its head office, Oxford, in September 2004. If you have what it takes to inspire others to change the world, there's no better place to do it. For more information, please visit Oxfam's website, www.oxfam.org.uk/graduate

inspire

Are you looking for a job where you can make a meaningful difference – and not just to your bank account? Could you inspire people to act against poverty? If you can answer yes to both, we'd love to hear from you.

Oxfam

Oxfam works with others to overcome poverty and suffering

www.oxfam.org.uk/graduate

Oxfam GB is a member of Oxfam International, registered charity no. 202918

PA Consulting Group

Vacancies for around 30 graduates in 2004

- Consulting
- Engineering
- Finance
- IT
- Research & Development

Starting salary in 2003
£31,000
Plus performance-related bonus.
Salary for 2004 has yet to be agreed.

Universities PA Consulting plan to visit in 2003-4
Aston, Bath, Birmingham, Cambridge, Edinburgh, Glasgow, Heriot-Watt, London, Loughborough, Manchester, Nottingham, Oxford, Strathclyde, UMIST
Please check with your university careers service for details of events.

Application deadline
12th December 2003

Contact Details
graduaterecruitment@paconsulting.com

Turn to Page 160 now to request more information about PA Consulting Group.

PA Consulting Group is a leading management, systems and technology consulting firm that works with clients from insight to implementation.

PA has won at the Management Consultancies Association awards for six straight years. They are an employee-owned company where they believe that all staff should be shareholders in the company. This philosophy has helped PA feature for the third year running as one of the Sunday Times' Top 100 companies to work for.

PA's IT, Decision Sciences and Technology and Innovation practices prefer IT-related, electronics, mechanical engineering, operational research and management science degrees. Their Strategy or Financial Services practices prefer statistical or finance-related degrees, and their Government practice prefers a politics-related degree. Please note that relevant work experience is desirable for all areas. For more information, please visit the PA web site.

An excellent academic record is essential (minimum 2.1 degree and 24 UCAS points), as is the ability to work co-operatively with others and present ideas effectively and persuasively. Graduates will also need a high degree of drive and tenacity, and ambition and business acumen are vital.

All graduates attend a three-week residential training programme, which focuses on developing their business, consulting and interpersonal skills. Optional courses enhance technical and non-technical skills and knowledge.

PA will provide graduates with ongoing training and development as well as on-the-job learning. They will also have support from their individual line manager and mentor.

PA Consulting Group

Look
closer...

Not all consulting firms are the same. PA Consulting Group works across the full spectrum of management, systems and technology consulting – operating from over 40 offices in more than 20 countries, and drawing on the knowledge and experience of around 3,300 people.

Everyone has the opportunity to earn equity in the firm, so we all think and act as owners, not just as employees. The fact that we create change for clients rather than merely proposing it has helped us win at the Management Consultancy Association (MCA) Best Management Practice Awards for six straight years. And it's probably worth mentioning that we recently featured for the third year running in *The Sunday Times 100 best companies to work for in the UK*.

For more information on graduate careers at PA, take a closer look at our web site.

PA is an equal opportunity employer.

Take a closer look at
www.paconsulting.com

PRICEWATERHOUSECOOPERS

www.pwc.com/uk/careers/

Vacancies for around 1,000 graduates in 2004

- Accountancy
- Consulting
- Finance
- Law

Starting salary for 2004
£Competitive
Plus flexible benefits and an interest-free loan

Universities that PwC plan to visit in 2003-4
Please check with your university careers service for details of events.

Application deadline
Early application is advised.
See website for further information.

Contact Details
☎ 0808 100 1500 /
+44 (0)121 265 5852
Turn to Page 160 now to request more information about PwC.

PricewaterhouseCoopers is the world's largest professional services organisation. With scores of industry-leading consulting and advisory groups, hundreds of offices around the world and thousands of exciting opportunities, the firm is the ideal springboard for any budding business professional.

The firm offers high-calibre graduates from any degree discipline a wide range of possibilities within the firm's business groups. These include Actuarial, Assurance & Business Advisory Services, Corporate Finance & Recovery, and Tax & Legal Services, each of which boasts an eye-catching client list. Some are renowned as breeding grounds for the best business minds in their field, whilst others are at the forefront of the challenging e-business arena.

PwC also offers a number of pre-graduate schemes and short-term contract opportunities for school leavers and undergraduates looking for an enlightening taster of life in Professional Services.

Depending on which part of the firm graduates join, they may study for qualification as a chartered accountant, or alternatively, tax associates often choose to prepare for the Institute of Taxation qualification. Graduates could become a qualified actuary, study for the Securities Institute Diploma, or qualify as a chartered financial analyst. Some joiners may even be eligible to study for an MBA or the CIPD qualification. Opportunities are nationwide.

The firm places great importance on the development of its people, both professionally and as individuals, and invests significant resources to provide first-class training which is available to staff throughout their careers. For more details, please refer to their website or brochures.

PUT YOUR CAREER INTO FOCUS
THEN MAKE THE CALL.

PRICEWATERHOUSE COOPERS [PW]

GRADUATE & UNDERGRADUATE OPPORTUNITIES – 2004
£COMPETITIVE & FLEXIBLE BENEFITS – NATIONWIDE

From Business Advisory, Strategic and Tax Consulting, Financial Advisory and Actuarial, through to Risk Management, we have over 20 different professional qualifications on offer across a variety of offices.

We also have a vast range of student and undergraduate programmes. So whether you've already decided where you're heading, or you've yet to fully consider your options, we're your perfect partner.

If you're a graduate with a good degree in any discipline, or are heading towards one, have a good academic background and want to find out more, please visit our website at:

www.pwc.com/uk/careers/

or you can call:

Freephone 0808 100 1500 or
tel: +44 (0)121 265 5852

Please quote ref. GRTT0209.

P&G

www.pgcareers.com

Vacancies for around 60 graduates in 2004

- Engineering
- Finance
- Human Resources
- IT
- Marketing
- Research & Development
- Sales

Vacancies also available in Europe

Starting salary for 2004
£26,000+

Universities that P&G plan to visit in 2003-4

Belfast, Birmingham, Cambridge, Dublin, Durham, Edinburgh, Leeds, London, Nottingham, Oxford, Strathclyde, Warwick
Please check with your university careers service for details of events.

Application deadline
See website for further information

Contact Details

✉ recunitedkingdm.im@pg.com
☎ 0800 056 5258 /
  +44 870 500 9013
Turn to Page 160 now to request more information about P&G.

Procter & Gamble's purpose is to provide products and services of superior quality and value that improve the lives of the world's consumers. As a result, consumers will reward the company with leadership sales and value creation, allowing P&G people, shareholders and the communities in which the company lives and works to prosper.

At the centre of these statements is one thought: people matter. To develop an organisation that is committed to winning and responsive to a world beyond commercial ambitions, P&G promote a working environment where corporate values are inseparable from individual values.

P&G market more than 250 brands and employ nearly 106,000 people in more than 80 countries worldwide. Their people-first culture encourages individuals from every nationality, race and background to create brilliant solutions together. Those attracted and recruited are the finest people in the world – they are the company's biggest asset and the guardians of their purpose, values and principles.

Everyone needs a life outside work. P&G has flexible work arrangements to meet those needs throughout your career. From part-time work to career breaks, from home working to job share, our people are finding new ways to combine great business results with a better work/life balance.

P&G recruit individualists – lateral thinkers – and seeks free spirits, who will be determined to take early responsibility and fulfil their potential. New employees can count on the company to give them the support and guidance they need to help them achieve their bold ambitions.

Procter&Gamble

careers at

Procter & Gamble

Anne Lambert joined P&G in September 1999 having completed a business course followed by a Masters Degree: "I thrived on the challenge and valued the help and support of my manager and my colleagues".

Imagine, just for a moment, your dream career...

Would it be...

...to work with a global organisation, offering truly international opportunities?

...where you can be yourself – not a corporate clone?

...in a culture which values its people above all else?

...where people are empowered to question, take risks and innovate?

...where technology and digital solutions redefine the future?

Now stop imagining. A career with Procter & Gamble offers all of this and more.

But, don't take our word for it – let our people tell you themselves.

To find out more about where the positions are located and other details, visit our recruitment website at www.PGcareers.com

We have opportunities available in the following business functions:

| Research & Development | Human Resources | Marketing |
| Finance | Product Supply | Information Technology |
| Customer Business Development |

www.PGcareers.com

QinetiQ

www.QinetiQ.com/careers

Put Pythagoras in a corner

Vacancies for around 300 graduates in 2004

■ Engineering
□ IT
■ Research & Development

Starting salary for 2004
Up to £21,000

Universities QinetiQ plans to visit in 2003-4
Bath, Belfast, Birmingham, Bristol, Cambridge, City, Edinburgh, Exeter, Glasgow, Heriot-Watt, Leeds, London, Manchester, Nottingham, Oxford, Southampton, Strathclyde, UMIST, Warwick, York
Please check with your university careers service for details of events.

Application deadline
Rolling Recruitment
Applying early is strongly recommended.

Contact Details
☎ +44 (0)8700 100 942
Turn to Page 160 now to request more information about QinetiQ.

If you're tired of hearing what the great minds thought, do some thinking of your own. If you're tired of studying science past, start creating some science history.

QinetiQ is Europe's largest science and technology organisation. A place where some of the world's leading research scientists combine to make the impossible an everyday commercial reality. Formed from part of DERA, the renowned UK Government R&D agency, it's a world leader in the creation and application of technology.

With over 7,000 people, including Europe's largest community of scientists, engineers and technicians, they have the facilities to tackle complex scientific problems in fields ranging from aerospace, security, defence and transport to media, healthcare, telecoms and finance.

QinetiQ offers a broad range of careers covering operational analysis, scientific research, development, test and evaluation and project management. QinetiQ looks for proactive, analytical, forward-thinking graduates from most science, engineering, IT and numerate disciplines – people with the commercial instinct, questioning mind and passion to take full advantage of this unique organisation.

QinetiQ offers a good salary and benefits package combined with real quality of life – the chance to do fascinating work in a pleasant environment. They provide the freedom, resources and training people need to push the boundaries of existing knowledge. Whether graduates want to follow a technical, business or project management route, they'll be surrounded by opportunities. But it will be up to the individual to take them.

REUTERS

www.reuters.com/careers/graduate

Vacancies for around
40 graduates in 2004

- Finance
- General Management
- IT
- Media

Vacancies also available in Europe

Starting salary for 2004
£Competitive

Universities that Reuters
plan to visit in 2003-4
Please check with your university
careers service for details of events.

Application deadline
31st December 2003

Contact Details

✉ community.manager@
reuters.com

Turn to Page 160 now to request
more information about Reuters.

Reuters is a leading global provider of news, financial information and technology solutions to financial institutions, the media, corporates and individuals.

Over 16,000 people work for Reuters in 97 countries and this is probably the most exciting period in Reuters' long history. They are breaking new ground and creating new traditions while maintaining their 150-year heritage. Graduates who are stimulated by continual challenge, and who want a career with variety without constantly switching companies, pinpoint Reuters as an employer of choice.

Reuters looks for a consistently strong academic track record and at least a 2.1 degree or equivalent. Other kinds of things are important too, such as evidence of mental agility, initiative, tenacity and the personality to do remarkable things. A healthy interest in the financial markets and web literacy is essential. Language requirements vary by programme. For Journalism and Business, fluency in English and one other language is essential. For Technology and Finance, fluency in English and working knowledge of another language is highly desirable.

The business of Reuters has many facets, and the training exposes graduates to as many of them as possible through assignments in different parts of their global organisation. The training for the e-world is arguably the best anywhere, providing a platform for creative ideas and limitless scope for graduates to make a real impact. But a word of warning to anyone who likes to deal in absolute certainties: in the Reuters world, there are none.

That's the fun of working in a dynamic organisation!

Rolls-Royce

www.rolls-royce.com/careers

Vacancies for around 100 graduates in 2004

- Engineering
- Finance
- Human Resources
- Logistics
- Purchasing

Starting salary for 2004
£22,000+

Universities Rolls-Royce plans to visit in 2003-4
Aston, Bath, Birmingham, Bristol, Cambridge, Cardiff, Dublin, London, Loughborough, Newcastle, Nottingham, Oxford, Sheffield, Southampton, Strathclyde, UMIST, Warwick
Please check with your university careers service for details of events.

Application deadline
Check website for deadline details

Contact Details
✉ careers@rolls-royce.com
Turn to Page 160 now to request more information about Rolls-Royce.

Time to think about your career. You'd love to carry on with your hobbies and interests, maybe do further study or voluntary work, perhaps travel, but you also want a quality training scheme with a top company. You want it all. How to square the circle?

Rolls-Royce is a global company providing power on land, sea and air. They offer graduate programmes in commercial, engineering, finance, HR, logistics, and purchasing. A Development Adviser works with graduates, guiding them in structuring an individual schedule of attachments and training activities, and there's also a mentor to help broaden graduates' outlook. It's a development programme but it's real work and real responsibility from the start.

So far, so good. But what about those other aspects of life that are also important? Rolls-Royce recruits a large number of graduates each year, and all their sites have an active social scene, so graduates are likely to meet someone who shares their interests. Various trainee associations organise a range of activities, so there's rarely a dull moment. Rolls-Royce also pay a decent salary, so graduates can afford to pursue their passions.

Recruits are strongly encouraged to achieve further relevant qualifications and membership of professional bodies. They'll also have the chance to be involved in education or community projects – a great way of challenging themselves whilst giving something back.

Rolls-Royce is a truly global company, so, whilst it isn't guaranteed, there's a good chance of an international element to graduates' training. Wherever the work, it's a complex and fascinating industry across land, sea and air.

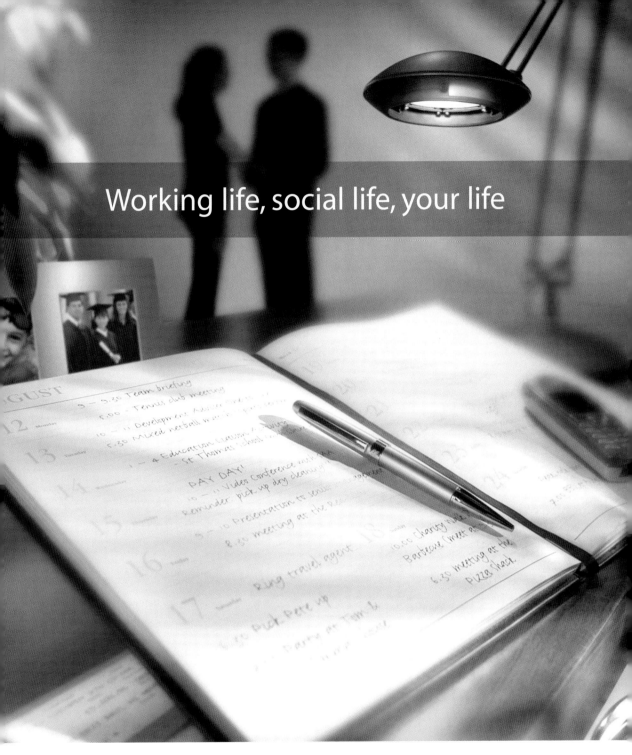

Working life, social life, your life

World-class. Quality. The very best.

These are some of the images conjured up by the Rolls-Royce name. And they don't just apply to our products and services. We offer world-class graduate training schemes, and we're looking for the very best candidates. Our programmes offer a quality experience - structured training based around real work, with support from a dedicated adviser and a mentor. That's just for starters. We're interested in the whole person. You'll be encouraged to undertake further professional study and personal development. You'll find an active social scene at all our sites, and you'll be given the opportunity to challenge yourself by getting involved in a community project. We're a truly global company, so there may even be the chance to spend some time abroad. **Trusted to deliver excellence**

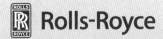 Rolls-Royce

ROYAL AIR FORCE ◎
RISE ABOVE THE REST

Vacancies for around 700 graduates in 2004

- Accountancy
- Engineering
- Finance
- General Management
- Human Resources
- IT
- Law
- Logistics

Vacancies also available in Europe, Asia and elsewhere in the world

Starting salary for 2004
£24,248-£26,798
After Initial Officer Training at the rank of Flying Officer

Universities the RAF plan to visit in 2003-4
Aberdeen, Aston, Bangor, Bath, Belfast, Birmingham, Bradford, Bristol, Brunel, Cambridge, Cardiff, City, Dundee, Durham, East Anglia, Edinburgh, Essex, Exeter, Glasgow, Heriot-Watt, Leeds, Leicester, Liverpool, London, Loughborough, Manchester, Newcastle, Northumbria, Nottingham, Nottingham Trent, Oxford, Oxford Brookes, Plymouth, Reading, Sheffield, Southampton, St Andrews, Stirling, Strathclyde, Surrey, Sussex, Swansea, Ulster, UMIST, Warwick, York

Application deadline
Rolling Recruitment
Applying early is strongly recommended.

Contact Details
☎ 0845 605 5555
Turn to Page 160 now to request more information about the RAF.

The Royal Air Force is the flying arm of the UK's Armed Forces. It offers 20 different commissioned officer careers over a wide range of disciplines, from Engineers to Air Traffic Controllers and Doctors to Caterers.

To be selected for officer training, candidates must demonstrate certain basic attributes that appropriate training can develop, including the potential to use initiative effectively, make decisions under pressure, and to lead by example.

Graduates begin their careers with the 24-week Initial Officer Training course at the RAF College Cranwell in Lincolnshire – although specialists undertake a shorter course, most newly-commissioned officers graduate in the rank of Flying Officer. Professional training follows, the length of which varies from branch to branch. Promotion to Flight Lieutenant is on a time and satisfactory service basis – usually within a couple of years; advancement to Squadron Leader and above is by competitive selection based on annual appraisals.

On completion of professional training, officers begin their first productive tour. For ground branch officers this normally lasts for about 18 months; aircrew tours tend to be longer. RAF operations and exercises, many of which are carried out in conjunction with the UN or NATO, may be conducted overseas; accordingly, all officers must be prepared to serve anywhere in the world.

An RAF officer career demands high standards and commitment. In return the RAF offers correspondingly high rewards; excellent career prospects, competitive salaries, a good pension scheme, free healthcare, ongoing professional management and personal development training, and wonderful opportunities for travel, sport and adventure.

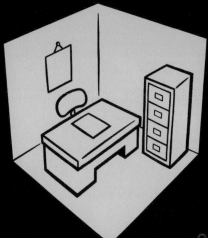

or **www.rafcareers.com**

don't work for a limited company **RAF** ⊙

RBS
The Royal Bank of Scotland Group

Vacancies for around 200 **graduates in 2004**

- Accountancy
- Consulting
- Finance
- General Management
- Human Resources
- Investment Banking
- IT
- Retailing
- Sales

Starting salary for 2004
£Competitive

Universities RBS Group plans to visit in 2003-4

Aberdeen, Bath, Birmingham, Bristol, Cambridge, Durham, Edinburgh, Glasgow, Leeds, London, Loughborough, Manchester, Newcastle, Nottingham, Oxford, Sheffield, Southampton, Stirling, Strathclyde, Warwick

Please check with your university careers service for details of events.

Application deadline
Rolling Recruitment

Applying early is strongly recommended.

Contact Details

✉ rbsgraduates@tmp.com

Turn to Page 160 now to request more information about the RBS Group.

Watch 'The Big Idea'. Four students, one goal, many ways to get there.

From Scottish high street bank to Europe's second largest financial institution, the fifth largest in the world. NatWest, Coutts & Co, Direct Line, Lombard Direct, The One Account and Tesco Personal Finance are all part of the Royal Bank of Scotland Group.

The Group has big ideas and makes them happen. It's all about change, flexibility, enterprise and doing things differently. The Royal Bank of Scotland Group is much more than traditional banking. It loves to think beyond it.

This attitude makes it many things to many graduates. Open minds from surprisingly varied backgrounds are welcomed and individually groomed to be future leaders of the Group. Flexible development programmes focus on specific needs and goals and last anything from 12 to 36 months, depending on which of the 11 different business areas a graduate enters. Expect a thorough induction, sponsorship for relevant professional qualifications and ongoing mentoring and support.

Above all, the Group looks for creative ideas and the ability to push the status quo and make them happen. Entrepreneurial flair, and a certain comfort with change, are important. Some graduates join after travelling or voluntary work, having honed well-rounded interpersonal skills.

The rewards package is excellent, even by normal financial sector standards. Perhaps the Group's approach to graduates is best illustrated in its award winning graduate film, a true reflection of the entrepreneurial essence of this forward-thinking employer. To experience the whole graduate application process online, visit www.rbs.co.uk/graduates

An action-packed adventure.

(And that's not just the film.)

Make it happen.

The Royal Bank of Scotland Group

www.rbs.co.uk/graduates

Sainsbury's
making life taste better

www.sainsburys.co.uk/forgetwhatyouthink

Vacancies for around
100-140 graduates in 2004

- Finance
- Human Resources
- Logistics
- Purchasing
- Retailing

Starting salary for 2004
£21,000
Subject to review

Universities Sainsbury's plan to visit in 2003-4
Aston, Bath, Belfast, Birmingham, Bristol, Cardiff, Durham, Lancaster, Leeds, Liverpool, London, Loughborough, Manchester, Newcastle, Nottingham, Oxford Brookes, Sheffield, Southampton, Strathclyde, Surrey, UMIST, Warwick
Please check with your university careers service for details of events.

Application deadline
12th January 2004
First deadline

Contact Details
✉ sainsburys@reed.co.uk
☎ 020 7384 7336
Turn to Page 160 now to request more information about Sainsbury's.

Forget what you think! Think you know Sainsbury's? Think again. Think you know retail? Think again – as well as retail management, Sainsbury's offer careers in buying, finance, supply chain, HR, pharmacy and quality & innovation.

Sainsbury's offer a variety of graduate programmes ranging from one-year schemes in buying to three-year schemes in retail and finance. All programmes ensure the correct mix of on-job experience, off-job training, development and professional qualifications where relevant.

Irrespective of the duration of the development scheme, graduates participate in a two-year training and development programme. Year one enables the building of management skills in areas such as impact and influence, team dynamics and personal awareness. Year two supports trainees in the areas of people and career management. These courses complement the additional training received specific to the function that graduates are working in.

All graduates are supported by fully trained line managers, mentors, buddies and cross-functional working party representatives. They'll also help manage performance and build a development plan. Naturally, graduates have even more success if this is supported with individual determination and drive.

Once in the business for nine months, graduates have the opportunity to apply for the Sainsbury's Corporate Leadership Programme, a 14 month scheme consisting of two seven month placements in different functions, which helps build project and general management capability. Sainsbury's also offers some placement opportunities for penultimate year students looking to broaden their work experience during a gap year or summer placement.

Think you know what's under the lid? Think again! Think you know what a career at Sainsbury's is all about? Think again! Our graduates are passionate about food and so much more – they're enjoying careers in retail management, buying, finance, human resources, supply chain, quality & innovation and pharmacy.

Forgotten your preconceptions yet? Excellent.
Take a look at our website and find out the real facts.

   We are committed to equal opportunities

 www.sainsburys.co.uk/forgetwhatyouthink

Sainsbury's
making life taste better

Schlumberger

www.slb.com/careers

**Vacancies for around
60 graduates in 2004**

- Engineering
- IT
- Research & Development

Vacancies also available
elsewhere in the world

Starting salary for 2004
£Competitive

**Universities Schlumberger
plans to visit in 2003-4**
Bath, Belfast, Birmingham,
Bristol, Cambridge, Dublin,
Heriot-Watt, Leeds, London,
Loughborough, Manchester,
Newcastle, Nottingham,
Oxford, Sheffield
Please check with your university
careers service for details of events.

Application deadline
Rolling Recruitment
Applying early is strongly
recommended.

Contact Details
Turn to Page 160 now to request
more information about
Schlumberger.

Schlumberger is a global technology services company with nearly 80,000 employees representing more than 100 nationalities. Schlumberger consists of two segments, Schlumberger Oilfield Services and SchlumbergerSema.

SchlumbergerSema is a major IT services company providing information technology consulting, systems integration, managed services, products and IP network security solutions serving the telecommunications, utility, finance, transport, oil and gas and public sector markets. It is also the world's foremost supplier of Smartcards and winners of the prestigious Management Consultancies Association Best Practice Award 2002.

Schlumberger Oilfield Services is a leading provider of services, solutions and technology to the international petroleum industry. They provide virtually every type of exploration, production and completion service needed in the petroleum industry.

Schlumberger's global reach offers a unique way of life that welcomes people from different backgrounds. Present in 100 countries with as many nationalities represented in their workforce, they are a culturally diverse community that provides one of the best environments for teamwork, innovation and value creation. Every year, they recruit and develop the best university graduates on a worldwide basis. After the graduate training program, their graduates can find themselves in a multitude of different roles and locations.

Their culture is based on the commitment of every Schlumberger person to deliver the best possible performance, anytime and anywhere, to achieve new standards of excellence that surpasses their customers' expectations.

Schlumberger | world ready :

"**It's bringing ideas from around the world to life before your eyes.**" Samantha, Project Manager

www.shell.com/careers

Vacancies for around 240 graduates in 2004
Across Europe

- Engineering
- Finance
- Human Resources
- IT
- Marketing
- Research & Development
- Sales

Vacancies also available in Europe and elsewhere in the world

Starting salary for 2004
£25,700
UK minimum only

Universities that Shell plans to visit in 2003-4

Aberdeen, Bath, Birmingham, Bristol, Cambridge, Dublin, Durham, Edinburgh, Glasgow, Heriot-Watt, Leeds, London, Loughborough, Manchester, Nottingham, Oxford, Sheffield, Southampton, UMIST
Please check with your university careers service for details of events.

Application deadline
Rolling Recruitment
Applying early is strongly recommended.

Contact Details

✉ graduates@shell.com

☎ 0845 600 1819

Turn to Page 160 now to request more information about Shell.

Shell is at the heart of the energy business, and is one of the world's most successful organisations. Shell offers international career prospects and outstanding challenges. Shell is also a part of society, and is therefore totally committed to a business strategy that always balances profits with principles.

From the moment graduates join Shell, their development is of prime importance. Learning by doing, supported by their manager, is key – real responsibility and decision-making are part of life at Shell from day one. Career progression depends entirely on individual ability, talent and ambition. Working for Shell, graduates could potentially move geographically, functionally and between different businesses. Shell have a strong ethic of promotion from within and a global job opportunity intranet site to support this.

Graduates' academic records are one key factor in assessing applications, but Shell also place emphasis on performance during interviews and assessment centres. Shell have identified capacity, achievement and relationships as critical to high performance.

Shell have a number of pre-employment opportunities: the Shell Business Challenge, for which applications are welcome from finalists during October and November 2003; placements, for which students in their penultimate year can apply during January and February 2004; and the Personal Development Award, for which applications are welcome from non-finalists during Spring 2004.

Full details on each of Shell's pre-employment and employment opportunities can be found on their website, www.shell.com/careers

Opportunities for Graduates

Who we are

Shell is at the heart of the energy business, and is one of the world's most successful organisations. Shell offers international career prospects and outstanding challenges. Shell is also a part of society, and is therefore totally committed to a business strategy that always balances profits with principles.

What we offer

A real job, with real responsibility inside a close team, is what we offer from the start - there's no 'one-size-fits all' trainee programme at Shell. What's more your contribution could really make a difference to society, through the daily challenges we face as an energy business. With the sheer scale of operation and number of different businesses, you'll have the opportunity to diversify, specialise, develop your career internationally or even change direction completely. You'll receive a tailored mix of on-the-job and structured training and, if it's appropriate to your role, full support through a professional qualification. What's more, your manager, your very own mentor and countless inspiring colleagues will be on hand to help.

Pre-Employment Opportunities

- The Shell Business Challenge (Applications are welcome from finalists during Autumn 2003)
- Placements (Applications are welcome from penultimate year students during Jan/Feb 2004)
- Personal Development Award (Applications are welcome from non-finalists during Spring 2004).

Find out more on **www.shell.com/careers**

Employment Opportunities

We have a broad range of opportunities in the following areas (there are no closing dates for employment applications);

- Engineering
- Technology Consultancy & Research
- Human Resources
- Sales & Marketing
- Finance
- IT

For technical roles you will be required to have a science or engineering degree.

Starting Salary £25,700 (UK minimum only).

Find Out More

For further information about Shell, our employment and pre-employment opportunities or to apply online please visit **www.shell.com/careers**, you can also email **graduates@shell.com** or call 0845 600 1819 if you have any queries. Please quote reference **4320**.

Thinking about a better future?
www.shell.com/careers

SLAUGHTER AND MAY

Vacancies for around
85 **graduates in 2004**
For training contracts commencing
September 2006 or March 2007.

■ **Law**

Starting salary
£29,000

**Universities that Slaughter
and May plan to visit in
2003-4**
Please check with your university
careers service for details of events.

Application deadline
Rolling Recruitment
Early application is strongly
recommended.

Contact Details
✉ grad.recruit@
    slaughterandmay.com
☎ 020 7600 1200
Turn to Page 160 now to request
more information on Slaughter and
May.

Slaughter and May is a leading international law firm whose principal areas of practice are in the fields of commercial, corporate and financial law.

The firm's clients include industrial and commercial companies, utilities, banks and financial institutions, professional firms and public bodies. They range from fledgling businesses to some of the world's biggest and most prestigious multinationals, from small regulatory bodies to governments and international institutions.

Much of Slaughter and May's work spans the globe with transactions involving not only the firm's overseas offices in Paris, Brussels, Singapore, Hong Kong and New York but also leading independent law firms in other jurisdictions around the world. There are opportunities for trainees to spend up to six months overseas on secondment.

Approximately 85 training contracts are available per year for trainee solicitors and Slaughter and May also offers placements during the Christmas, Easter and summer vacations for those considering a career in law.

Following Law School, there is a two year training period during which time trainee solicitors gain experience of a broad cross-section of the firm's practice by taking an active part in the work of four or five departments, sharing an office with a partner or experienced associate. In addition, Slaughter and May offers an extensive training programme of lectures, seminars and courses.

Applications from undergraduates of good 2.1 ability from any discipline are considered. Please visit their website for further information.

We've built our firm on the sharing of knowledge and experience in an informal and friendly atmosphere. Whatever legal problems you come across – in your training or subsequently – you'll find someone who's already an expert, and is ready and willing to share the relevant knowledge with you.

Unrestrictive practice.

SLAUGHTER AND MAY

Teach First
LEARNING TO LEAD

Vacancies for around 200 graduates in 2004

■ **All sectors**

Please visit the Teach First
website for further details.

Starting salary for 2004
£Competitive

**Universities Teach First
plans to visit in 2003-4**

Bath, Birmingham, Bristol,
Brunel, Cambridge, Cardiff,
Durham, Edinburgh, Glasgow,
Leeds, London, Manchester,
Nottingham, Oxford, Sheffield,
Strathclyde, UMIST, Warwick.
Please check with your university
careers service for details of events.

Application deadline
Year-round recruitment
Applying early is strongly
recommended.

Contact Details
Turn to Page 160 now to request
more information about Teach First.

Thought about teaching, but not yet sure of it as a career?
Looking to work in industry, government or for a nonprofit
organisation, but not just yet?

Teach First is an independent programme for top graduates who want to be
tomorrow's leaders while making an impact today. Participants spend two
years teaching in challenging secondary schools in London and receive
education training from Canterbury Christ Church University College and over
forty top supporting employers, many of which are in this book.

During year one, participants are trained to become outstanding teachers with
Qualified Teacher Status. In year two, participants take part in internships with
supporters, and receive leadership training through Teach First's 'mini-MBA'
programme, Learning to Lead. After two years, Teach First alumni can stay on
in teaching, or move into other sectors, using their experience and skills to
become influential leaders of industry, government, or in the nonprofit sector.

It can be tough working in challenging schools, which is why participants are
placed in teams of around four, and receive layers of support, including
in-school mentors and experienced personal tutors. Business mentors guide
participants in making informed career choices and to help them gain insights
into the pros, cons and practicalities of succeeding in different careers.

Teach First is not for everybody. Few possess the communication skills,
initiative, self-confidence, intelligence, and humility you need to succeed on the
programme. But its blend of real impact and leadership training has struck a
chord with today's graduates. Perhaps this why Teach First is one of the
highest ranking new employers to enter the Times Top 100 this year.

In an uncertain world, it is hard figuring out how to make your mark. Governments and markets rise and fall, today's hard work can easily disappear on the whim of a CEO, Minister, or trader. As a participant on the Teach First programme, you can **make** a real difference in the most strategic way possible on the lives of children in some of the most challenging secondary schools in London. Discover your power to change lives forever, to influence and make decisions that will endure. Best of all, you can keep your options wide open while making **a difference**. With Teach First's top business and non-business sponsors, training, mentoring, and support, you will gain the skills, character, and networks, to make a difference whatever you choose to do after just two years of teaching.

Make a difference while keeping your options open.
Find out more and apply online at www.teachfirst.org.uk

Teach**First**
LEARNING TO LEAD

TESCO

Vacancies for around 120 graduates in 2004

- Accountancy
- Finance
- General Management
- Human Resources
- IT
- Marketing
- Media
- Purchasing
- Research & Development
- Retailing

Starting salary for 2004
£18,500-£24,500

Universities that Tesco plans to visit in 2003-4
Aston, Cardiff, London, Loughborough, Manchester, Nottingham, Reading, Sheffield, Southampton, Strathclyde, Swansea, UMIST, Warwick
Please check with your university careers service for details of events.

Application deadline
13th January 2004

Contact Details
✉ graduate.recruitment@uk.tesco.com
☎ 0870 600 6067
Turn to Page 160 now to request more information on Tesco.

Want to work for a multi-national, market-leading company with diverse career prospects? Then look no further than Tesco.

With over 750 stores and 200,000 employees, it's the country's largest private sector employer, and is experiencing rapid international expansion. Furthermore, Tesco is committed to being as successful in non-food as it is in food: Tesco.com is the world's most successful on-line retailer; stores retail products such as clothing, DVDs and electrical goods, and they continue to launch new products and services from mobile phones to financial services.

Tesco look for graduates with a unique blend of people, leadership and analytical skills. They need a passion for the industry and the ability to rise to the challenge of working in the exciting world of retail. Able to make decisions quickly, graduates should be flexible in their approach and comfortable with Tesco's demanding, ever-changing but ultimately supportive environment. Graduates benefit from exposure to all areas of the business as well as hands-on experience mixed with workshops, theory and personal skills development.

Tesco recruit into three schemes. Store Management aims to see graduates progress to Store Manager within five years and be responsible for up to 800 staff and a £50million turnover. The Specialist Management scheme sees graduates join in a key business function such as Finance, IT, Tesco.com or Insight, developing in-depth knowledge and understanding. And in the General Management scheme, graduates focus on becoming Retail Business Managers in areas such as Commercial, Corporate Affairs and Marketing.

Tesco offer annual career planning and a continually revised personal development plan offering opportunities to transfer into other functions.

Glastonbury
or
Creamfields?

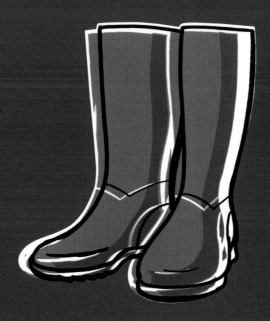

**It's time to make decisions
that really matter...**

www.tesco.com/graduates

www.ubs.com/graduates

Vacancies for around
80-100 graduates in 2004

- Finance
- Investment Banking
- IT
- Logistics

Vacancies also available in
Europe and Asia

Starting salary for 2004
£30,000-£35,000

Universities that UBS
plans to visit in 2003-4
Please check with your university
careers service for details of events.

Application deadline
14th November 2003

Contact Details
Turn to Page 160 now to request
more information about UBS.

UBS is one of the world's leading financial firms, serving a discerning global client base. As an organisation, it combines financial strength with a global culture that embraces change.

It is the world's leading provider of wealth management services. In the investment banking and securities businesses, it is among the select bracket of major global houses. UBS is also one of the largest asset managers globally. In Switzerland, it is the clear market leader, serving corporate and retail clients. As an integrated firm, UBS creates added value for clients by drawing on the combined resources and expertise of all its businesses.

With head offices in Zurich and Basel, and more than 68,000 employees, UBS operates in over 50 countries and in all major international financial centres. UBS offers graduate and summer internship positions across all its businesses, mainly based in London.

Academic credentials are important but need to be coupled with excellent communication skills, creativity, perseverance and tenacity. Also, research of a desired business area is key, whether utilising the wealth of information to be found on the internet or speaking to those already working in the industry.

UBS offers a ten week structured summer programme, which is a vital tool in the recruitment process. Those chosen will work alongside the best, learning about the organisation, the business area they are in and the products and clients with which UBS deals. There will be events throughout that will ensure the experience is packed with learning, networking and training opportunities. Evaluation will also be a serious element of the programme and, if successful, UBS will offer a permanent graduate position for the following year.

Ning Zhang / Equity Sales / Hong Kong

Unlimited global career opportunities

UBS is a leading global financial services firm with a diverse client base ranging from affluent individuals to governments, multinational institutions and corporations. We are an integrated group encompassing investment banking, asset management and wealth management as well as retail and corporate banking.

It's true that building a career in financial services is a demanding option. You'll need a strong personality, an ability to learn and think quickly and the determination to excel. The return on your investment will be a truly rewarding career with unlimited opportunities.

With over 70,000 people delivering our outstanding services and products in 50 countries, UBS is looking for individuals from different backgrounds – with a range of perspectives, experiences and skills – to reflect the depth and breadth of our client base.

If this is your last summer before graduation and you are focusing on an internship, this is your chance to make it count. If you are ready to begin a full-time career, now is the time to take your first steps towards a great future.

The closing dates for graduate applications are:

14 November 2003	Equities, Fixed Income, Rates and Currencies, Investment Banking Department, Information Technology and Global Asset Management
28 November 2003	Operations and Human Resources

Applications for Wealth Management International (formerly known as Private Banking) are accepted all year round.

The closing date for internship applications is:

13 February 2004

We encourage you to apply as early as possible.

All applications must be made online.

If you think you've got what it takes, log on to find out more:

www.ubs.com/graduates

Diversity, one of our core values at UBS, is essential to our global success and that of our clients. To this end, we foster an innovative, flexible culture rooted in respect, ensuring that all talented UBS employees have the opportunity to thrive. As a result, we attract and retain open-minded, dedicated employees, each bringing a multitude of diverse perspectives to the firm. By embracing diversity of cultures, skills and experiences, we create long-term value for our employees, clients and shareholders.

Wealth Management | Global Asset Management | Investment Bank

 UBS

Unilever

Vacancies for around
60 graduates in 2004

- Engineering
- Finance
- Human Resources
- IT
- Logistics
- Marketing
- Research & Development
- Sales

Starting salary for 2004
c£24,000

Universities Unilever
plans to visit in 2003-4
Aston, Bath, Birmingham,
Bristol, Cambridge, Durham,
Edinburgh, Exeter, Glasgow,
Leeds, London, Manchester,
Newcastle, Nottingham,
Oxford, Sheffield, Strathclyde,
UMIST, Warwick
Please check with your university
careers service for details of events.

Application deadline
14th December 2003

Contact Details
✉ enquiry@go-ucmds.com
☎ 0870 154 3550
Turn to Page 160 now to request more
information about Unilever.

Unilever is one of the world's leading consumer goods companies. Its brands, including Dove, Magnum, Persil and Lynx, are used by over half the families in the world every day.

Meeting their consumers' needs is the company's number one priority – constantly adapting to develop new products, improve established brands and pioneer more creative and flexible ways of working.

While a degree is important, Unilever is more interested in the qualities that make outstanding leaders. These include being passionate about business – inspired by profit, competition and customer satisfaction. It also means being ambitious, entrepreneurial and acting with integrity.

Unilever's two year programme, UCMDS, is designed to develop graduates' skills to help them reach senior management in the shortest possible time. Graduates join a UK operating unit in their chosen function, where they will have a real job and real responsibility from the outset. They can expect an excellent development programme, usually consisting of four placements with the opportunity to spend time outside their chosen function. There are also opportunities to work abroad within the first three years and comprehensive training covering personal development, general business and professional skills.

Full support is given to gain relevant professional qualifications and chartered status – Unilever accredited training programmes include CIMA, IMechE, IChemE and IEE – and there is a strong support network including a buddy, mentor and senior sponsor, as well as ongoing coaching from line managers.

Kirstine Lawson
UCMDS trainee

Kirstine's drive helped her to achieve over half a million pounds cost saving for the business.

Your passion. Our strength

At Unilever, it's the passion, creativity and skill of our people that drive our success. We believe that as you develop and grow, so will our business. Across our global operations, people with talent, integrity and the ambition to win, fulfil their potential in an environment where individuality is respected and new ideas flourish.

Find out more at www.ucmds.com

Unilever

you

How are you?

www.vodafone.co.uk/graduates

Vacancies for around 70 **graduates in 2004**

- Engineering
- Finance
- IT
- Marketing
- Sales

Starting salary for 2004
£21,000-£25,000

Universities Vodafone plan to visit in 2003-4
Please visit Vodafone's website or check with your university careers service for details of events.

Application deadline
Please visit Vodafone's website for deadline information.

Contact Details

✉ graduate.resourcing@vf.vodafone.co.uk

☎ 0700 267 7779

Turn to Page 160 now to request more information on Vodafone.

As the world's leading mobile telecoms company with more than 113 million customers in 28 countries, Vodafone continues to revolutionise the way people live, generating a continuous flux of new and innovative services for people on the move. They are helping people everywhere to communicate, manage, organise, pay and play as part of a full-colour, mobile world.

Vodafone need graduates with the vision to challenge the status quo and come up with progressive ideas – people with the ambition to scale a steep learning curve and the flexibility to embrace a culture of change. With a 2.1 or better, graduates could establish a breadth and depth of specialist expertise, as well as genuine project ownership.

A rich mixture of formal training through their acclaimed 'Unlock your Potential' programme and flexible hands-on learning will equip graduates with an understanding of Vodafone's core business and an overview of the commercial environment in which they operate. A series of placements across the business will allow graduates to broaden their skills base – and by working closely with experienced professionals they will gain exposure to a variety of techniques first hand. Vodafone will give all the support needed to study for a professional qualification and they also run a wide range of supplementary development courses – from presentation skills to the Duke of Edinburgh Award for Business.

Whatever graduates' ambitions are, there's a good chance Vodafone can put them on the right track. To learn with the experts and share in the success of one of the world's most vibrant industries, find out more on their website.

Some people think beyond their job description.

Technology/Marketing/Finance/Sales/R&D

The people who drive change are the ones who don't wait for instructions. They're people who think about what they're doing in a wider context – people with the drive and aptitude to take on new responsibilities and get things done. And in return they're rewarded not only with the chance to progress into management early on in their careers, but to go down in history as one of the people who helped to revolutionise the way we communicate. Do you fit the description?

www.vodafone.co.uk/graduates

vodafone

Watson Wyatt
Worldwide

www.watsonwyatt.com/graduate

Vacancies for around
60 **graduates in 2004**

■ **Consulting**

▨ **Finance**

Vacancies also available in Europe

Starting salary for 2004
£Competitive

Universities Watson Wyatt plan to visit in 2003-4
Bath, Belfast, Bristol,
Cambridge, Durham,
Edinburgh, Heriot-Watt,
London, Manchester,
Nottingham, Oxford, Sheffield,
UMIST, Warwick, York
Please check with your university
careers service for details of events.

Application deadline
Rolling Recruitment
Applying early is strongly
recommended.

Contact Details

✉ **graduate.recruitment@**
   eu.watsonwyatt.com

☎ **01737 241144**

Turn to Page 160 now to request
more information on Watson Wyatt.

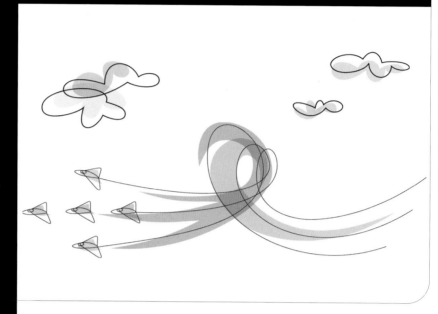

A global consulting firm, Watson Wyatt focuses on human capital and financial management to deliver business solutions that drive shareholder value.

It's one of the world's most influential professional services organisations, working with over 50 of the top 100 UK corporate pension funds and 73 per cent of the Fortune 500 Global companies headquartered in Britain, creating value through people and for people. Watson Wyatt has been in the 'Sunday Times Top 100 companies to work for' for three years running.

The firm's expertise spans Benefits, Human Capital, Insurance and Financial Services and Investment. They also have practices dedicated to Benefits Administration Solutions and E-solutions.

This offers graduates the scope to develop a broad skills base through formal and practical training. The aim here is to develop 'thought-leaders', which is why graduates are given the time and resources to build their expertise, as well as the responsibility for managing both.

To join in an actuarial or investment consulting capacity, graduates must have a numerate degree. For HR consulting, a business or HR-related degree is needed. Graduates from any discipline can join the Benefits Administration Solutions team. In all cases though, candidates must have a first-class or upper second-class degree, as well as 300 UCAS points (or equivalent).

For more information about the impressive performance-related rewards and international career opportunities available at Watson Wyatt, and to apply online, please visit www.watsonwyatt.com/graduate

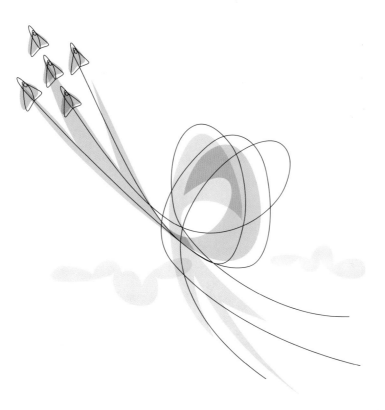

BREADTH OF EXPERTISE

Many strengths, all working together. That's how, at Watson Wyatt, we have established ourselves as one of the world's most influential professional services firms.

To maintain our momentum, we are committed to developing our people, acquiring new skills, staying ahead of the challenges businesses face and responding innovatively to a rapidly changing world. It's no wonder that we have appeared in the 'Sunday Times best 100 companies to work for', three years running.

We are advisers to 73% of the Fortune Global 500 companies headquartered in Britain and consulting actuaries to over 50 of the UK's top 100 corporate pension schemes. We invest in graduates with intellectual capacity to become the next generation of thought leaders. And we help all our people to put their expanding knowledge to work – for us, for our clients and for themselves.

We provide the resources for graduates to build their expertise alongside recognised leaders in their field. Our approach unites people from a wide range of nationalities and backgrounds. The diverse skills of our people add to the Watson Wyatt career experience.

How will our investment in your future influence you? Start by visiting our careers information point at www.watsonwyatt.com/graduate

WPP

**Vacancies for around
10 graduates in 2004**

■ Marketing

■ Media

Vacancies also available in Europe
and elsewhere in the world

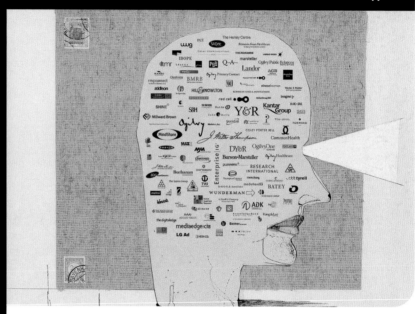

Starting salary for 2004
£22,000-£27,000

**Universities WPP
plans to visit in 2003-4**
Bristol. Cambridge.
Edinburgh. London. Oxford.
Please check with your university
careers service for details of events.

Application deadline
3rd December 2003

Contact Details
✉ hmiller@wpp.com
☎ 020 7408 2204
Turn to Page 160 now to request more
information about WPP.

WPP is one of the world's largest communications services groups, made up of leading companies in advertising, media investment management, information, insight & consultancy, public relations & public affairs, branding & identity, healthcare, direct, promotion & relationship marketing and specialist communications.

Through its 90 companies, WPP provides communications services to national, multinational and global clients, including more than 330 of the Fortune Global 500 and over one half of the NASDAQ 100. Its 62,000 people work out of 1,400 offices in 103 countries.

WPP Marketing Fellowships, which develop high-calibre management talent with experience across a range of marketing disciplines, will be awarded to applicants who graduate in 2004. Those selected will work in a number of WPP companies and across different marketing disciplines.

WPP is offering several three year Fellowships, multi-disciplinary experience, competitive remuneration and excellent long term career prospects within a WPP company. WPP wants people who are committed to marketing, who take a rigorous and creative approach to problem-solving, who are curious and will function well in a flexible, loosely structured work environment.

The first year of the Fellowship is spent working in a WPP sponsoring company and a personal mentor is assigned to provide overall career guidance. Thereafter, each individual will spend 18 to 24 months working in one or two other WPP companies, with each chosen on the basis of the individual's interests and the Group's needs.

Ambidextrous brains required

WPP is one of the world's leading communications services groups. Major brands include J. Walter Thompson, Ogilvy & Mather, Young & Rubicam, MindShare, Mediaedge:cia, Millward Brown, OgilvyOne, Wunderman, Hill & Knowlton, Burson-Marsteller, Ogilvy Public Relations, Cohn & Wolfe, CommonHealth, Enterprise IG and Landor, among others.

Their specialist skills include advertising, media investment management, information, insight & consultancy, public relations & public affairs, branding & identity, healthcare, direct, promotion & relationship marketing and specialist communications: disparate

disciplines with two common factors. They are all in business to contribute to the success of their clients. And they all do so through a demanding combination of flair and slog; intuition and logic; left brain and right brain.

WPP is offering a number of WPP Marketing Fellowships to applicants who will graduate in 2004. Those selected will work in a number of WPP companies and across different marketing disciplines. Excellent long-term career prospects within a WPP company.

Information leaflets are available from:
Harriet Miller at WPP, 27 Farm Street, London W1J 5RJ
T +44(0)20 7408 2204 F +44(0)20 7493 6819
E-mail: hmiller@wpp.com

Deadline for entry: 3 December 2003

visit our website www.wpp.com

Enter our free prize draw to win £5,000 in cash!

Make use of our free information service to find out more about the employers featured within this edition of **The Times Top 100 Graduate Employers,** and you could be £5,000 richer when you start your first job!

All you need to do is complete the special **Information Request** card that appears opposite and send it back before the closing date, **31st March 2004.**

Or you can register your details online at **www.Top100GraduateEmployers.com**

Every completed request card or online registration will be entered into a special prize draw to win the £5,000 in cash.

The information that you request will be despatched to you from the employers directly. The service is entirely free to all UK students and recent graduates.

Fill in the card or go to www.Top100GraduateEmployers.com now!
The first 1,000 requests received will win a mouse-mat from The Times.

THE ✠ TIMES

TOP 100

GRADUATE EMPLOYERS

INFORMATION REQUEST 2003/2004

To request further information about the employers featured in The Times Top 100 Graduate Employers and enter our free prize draw to win £5,000, just complete your details below and return this postcard.

Your information will be despatched to you directly from the employers, either by email, post or text message via your mobile phone.

NAME _Kenneth Yim_

UNIVERSITY _Oxford Brookes_

COURSE _Intelligent Systems_

TERMTIME ADDRESS

MIOD, Morrell Hall

John Garne Way

Marston, Oxford OX3 0TU

EMAIL _03105013@brookes.ac.uk_

MOBILE TEL. NO. _07776853319_

☑ PRE-FINAL YEAR ☐ FINAL YEAR ☐ I'VE ALREADY GRADUATED

Please tick the sectors that you would most like to work in:

ACCOUNTANCY . . . . ☐
CONSULTING . . . . ☑
ENGINEERING . . . . ☐
FINANCE . . . . ☐
GENERAL MANAGEMENT . . . ☐
HUMAN RESOURCES . . . . . ☐
INVESTMENT BANKING . . . . ☐
IT . . . . ☑
LAW . . . . ☐
LOGISTICS . . . . ☐
MARKETING . . . . ☐
MEDIA . . . . ☐
LOGISTICS . . . . ☐
RESEARCH & DEVELOPMENT ☐
RETAILING . . . . ☐
SALES . . . . ☐

Please tick the organisations you would like information from:

ABN AMRO	☐	L'ORÉAL ☐
ACCENTURE	☑	LINKLATERS ☐
AIRBUS	☐	LLOYDS TSB ☐
ALDI	☐	MARKS & SPENCER ☐
ALLEN & OVERY	☐	MASTERFOODS ☐
ARCADIA GROUP	☐	MCDONALD'S RESTAURANTS ☐
ARMY	☐	MERCER HR CONSULTING ☐
ASDA	☐	MI5: THE SECURITY SERVICE ☐
ASTRAZENECA	☑	MICROSOFT ☑
BAE SYSTEMS	☐	MINISTRY OF DEFENCE ☐
BARCLAYS	☐	MORGAN STANLEY ☐
BDO STOY HAYWARD	☐	NESTLÉ ☐
BNFL	☐	NHS ☐
BT	☑	OXFAM ☐
CADBURY SCHWEPPES	☐	PA CONSULTING GROUP ☑
CIVIL SERVICE OF N IRELAND	☐	PRICEWATERHOUSECOOPERS ☐
CREDIT SUISSE FIRST BOSTON	☑	PROCTER & GAMBLE ☐
DELOITTE	☐	QINETIQ ☐
DIAGEO	☐	REUTERS ☐
DLA	☐	ROLLS-ROYCE ☐
DSTL	☐	ROYAL AIR FORCE ☐
ERNST & YOUNG	☐	ROYAL BANK OF SCOTLAND GP ☐
EVERSHEDS	☐	SAINSBURY'S ☐
EXXONMOBIL	☐	SCHLUMBERGER ☑
GCHQ	☐	SHELL ☐
GLAXOSMITHKLINE	☐	SLAUGHTER & MAY ☐
GOLDMAN SACHS	☐	TEACH FIRST ☐
GRANT THORNTON	☐	TESCO ☐
HBOS	☐	UBS ☐
HSBC	☐	UNILEVER ☐
IBM	☑	VODAFONE ☐
JAGUAR / LAND ROVER	☐	WATSON WYATT ☐
KPMG	☐	WPP ☐

THE INSTITUTE OF CHARTERED ACCOUNTANTS IN ENGLAND & WALES

The closing date to request information from these employers and be included in the prize draw to win £5,000 is **Wednesday 31st March 2004.** If you do **not** wish to be included on our general mailing list and receive information from other relevant graduate employers, please tick here ☐

THE TIMES

TOP 100

GRADUATE EMPLOYERS

Find out more about Britain's top graduate employers and you could start your career £5,000 richer!